metrobasel

REGION IS AN URBAN
AGGLOMERATION CONSISTING
OF THE CORE CITY OF BASEL,
ITS SUBURBS, AND THE RURAL
CATCHMENT AREAS.

metrobasel

IS THE IDENTITY UNIFYING THE
TRINATIONAL METROPOLITAN
REGION OF BASEL.

THIS IS A STORY ABOUT
METROBASEL...

IT IS A LOVELY SUNDAY AFTERNOON. PATRICIA, AN ARCHITECT LIVING IN BASEL, IS RETURNING FROM A WEEKEND IN PARIS.

SEAT 12B... TOO BAD, NO WINDOW SEAT! ..HMM..

MICHEL, A CAR SALESMAN FROM PARIS, IS ON THE SAME FLIGHT

12A. GREAT. A WINDOW SEAT. I'LL BE ABLE TO LOOK OUT...

HI, JE SUIS MICHEL.

OH DEAR, I HOPE HE DOESN'T BUG ME....

...AFTER THEY HAVE FOUND THEIR SEATS...

SOON THE PLANE TAKES OFF. MICHEL GLANCES OUT OF THE WINDOW.

WWWRRRROOOMMMM

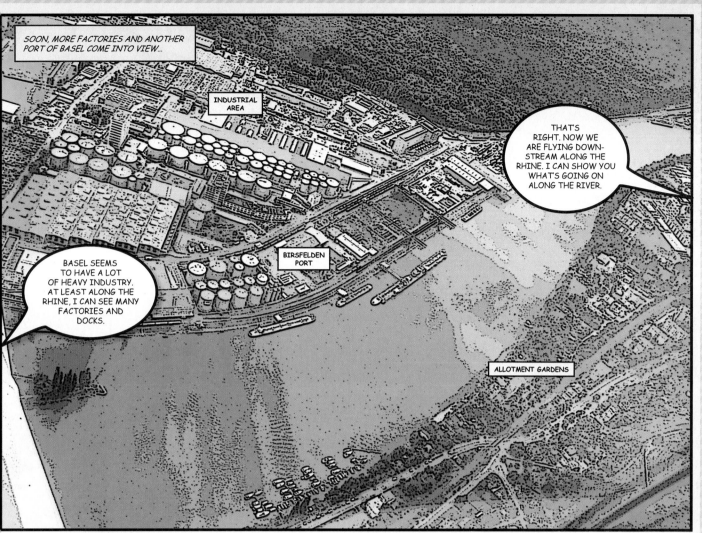

SOON, MORE FACTORIES AND ANOTHER PORT OF BASEL COME INTO VIEW...

INDUSTRIAL AREA

THAT'S RIGHT. NOW WE ARE FLYING DOWN-STREAM ALONG THE RHINE. I CAN SHOW YOU WHAT'S GOING ON ALONG THE RIVER.

BIRSFELDEN PORT

BASEL SEEMS TO HAVE A LOT OF HEAVY INDUSTRY. AT LEAST ALONG THE RHINE, I CAN SEE MANY FACTORIES AND DOCKS.

ALLOTMENT GARDENS

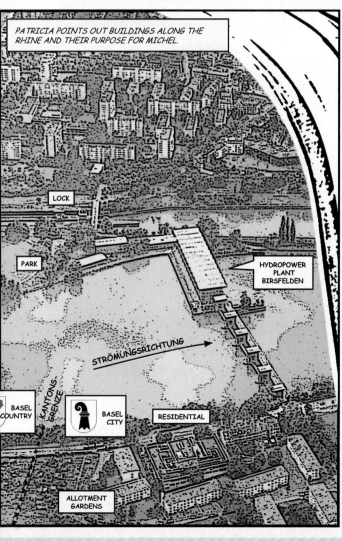

PATRICIA POINTS OUT BUILDINGS ALONG THE RHINE AND THEIR PURPOSE FOR MICHEL.

LOCK

PARK

HYDROPOWER PLANT BIRSFELDEN

STRÖMUNGSRICHTUNG

BASEL COUNTRY

KANTONS-GRENZE

BASEL CITY

RESIDENTIAL

ALLOTMENT GARDENS

WE JUST CROSSED THE CANTONAL BOUNDARY AND ARE FLYING ABOVE THE CANTON OF BASEL CITY..

..THE METROBASEL REGION CONSISTS OF MANY ADMINISTRATIVE UNITS AND BOUNDARIES.

5

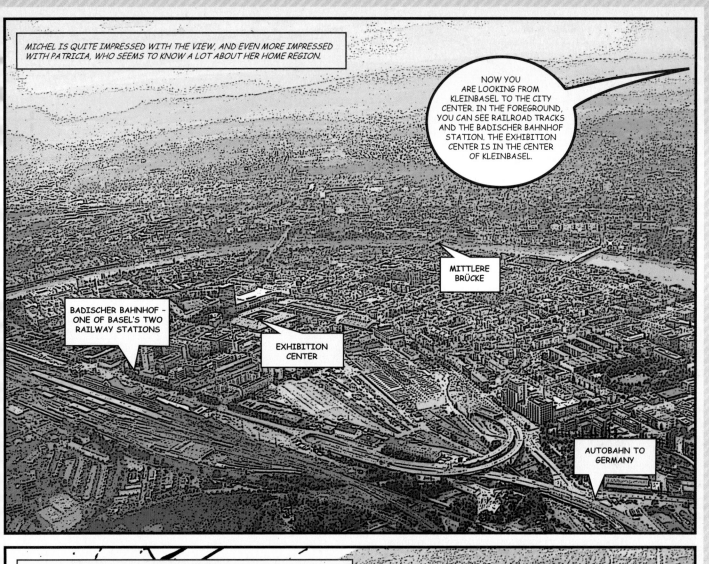

THE PLANE IS ALREADY FLYING QUITE LOW AND APPROACHING TO LAND.

THIS IS THE VIEW OF THE ENTIRE REGION LOOKING SOUTHWARDS.

AND TURNING EAST, THE GAZE ONCE MORE TAKES IN ALL THREE COUNTRIES.

LOOK. YOU CAN SEE ALL THREE COUNTRIES AT ONCE, WITH THE BLACK FOREST FOOTHILLS IN THE BACKGROUND REACHING ALL THE WAY DOWN TO BASEL. WAY BACK IN THE HAZE YOU CAN SEE THE PEAKS OF THE JURA. WE ARE OVERFLYING THE SPUR OF THE SUNDGAU, THE THIRD GEOGRAPHICAL LANDSCAPE THAT HAS GIVEN SHAPE TO METROBASEL.

..NEXT DAY AT NOON, ON THE MARKET SQUARE IN BASEL...

OH, HI MICHEL! WHAT A COINCIDENCE TO SEE YOU HERE.

PATRICIA! GREAT TO SEE YOU AGAIN.

THANKS AGAIN FOR ALL THE INTERESTING THINGS YOU POINTED OUT ON THE PLANE YESTERDAY. I WAS VERY IMPRESSED!

...HE SEEMS TO BE REALLY NICE...

OH YES! THAT SOUNDS VERY INTERESTING. I HAPPEN TO BE FREE AND WOULD LOVE TO KNOW MORE ABOUT YOUR CITY...

...SHE'S REALLY CHARMING...

I HAPPEN TO BE VISITING SOME FRIENDS AT AN INSTITUTE ON URBANISM NEARBY. YOU'RE WELCOME TO COME ALONG IF YOU ARE INTERESTED.

THE RED CITY HALL OF BASEL, BUILT 1504-1514, EXPANDED IN 1898.

A FEW MINUTES LATER ON SPITALSTRASSE, OUTSIDE ETH STUDIO BASEL

GREAT. THEN WHY DON'T WE GO INSIDE AND MEET THEM.

ETH STUDIO BASEL HAS BEEN WORKING FOR SEVERAL YEARS ON PROJECTS AND IDEAS FOR BASEL AND THE TRI-NATIONAL REGION. MY STUDENT FRIENDS KNOW ALL ABOUT IT.

11

75ZG0063

630 kg 8 pers.

EVERY SEMESTER, ETH STUDIO BASEL* STUDIES A CITY WHICH THE STUDENTS ANALYZE AND DESCRIBE.

*ETH STUDIO BASEL WAS FOUNDED IN 1999 BY ROGER DIENER, JACQUES HERZOG, MARCEL MEILI, AND PIERRE DE MEURON. IT IS PART OF THE ARCHITECTURE DEPARTMENT AT ETH ZURICH, BUT LOCATED IN BASEL.

3.06 ETH Studio Basel *

VIEW OF THE COURTYARD, WHERE MORE ARCHITECTURE OFFICES ARE LOCATED.

IN THE SPACE OF THE INSTITUTE...

ETH STUDIO BASEL IS AN INSTITUTE OF URBANISM. ITS RESEARCH HAS BEEN PUBLISHED IN A NUMBER OF BOOKS.*

MY FRIEND LEOPOLD IS GOING TO EXPLAIN THE BASIC ASPECTS OF THE REGION FOR US...

The Canary Islands

OPEN— CLOSED

An urban research study on the Canary Islands

Die Schweiz
Ein städtebauliches Portrait

Einführung

Roger Diener
Jacques Herzog
Marcel Meili
Pierre de Meuron
Christian Schmid

ETH Studio Basel
Institut Stadt der Gegenwart

*ETH STUDIO BASEL PUBLICATIONS::
- "DIE SCHWEIZ: EIN STÄDTEBAULICHES PORTRAIT"; BIRKHÄUSER, 2005
- "OPEN - CLOSED"; ETH STUDIOBASEL, 2007
- "THURGAU: PROJEKTE FÜR DIE STILLEN ZONEN"; NIGGLI VERLAG, 2008
- "BELGRAD: FORMAL / INFORMAL"; FORTHCOMING 2009

LEOPOLD, A DIPLOMA STUDENT, IS PREPARING AN INTRODUCTION TO THE REGION AND THE CITY CENTER, AND HAS ALSO INVITED A FEW EXPERTS.

HMMMM... LET'S SEE HOW I CAN STRUCTURE THE INTRODUCTION...

FIRST OF ALL, I'LL TALK ABOUT THE BASIC ELEMENTS OF THE REGION - THE RHINE AND THE DIFFERENT LANDSCAPES.

THE RHINE AND LANDSCAPES - PAGES 14 & 15.

NEXT, I SHOULD PROBABLY GIVE A HISTORICAL OVERVIEW.

THE HISTORY OF METRO-BASEL: PAGES 16-22.

THEN I'LL PRES-ENT THE HISTORY OF BASEL'S URBAN PLAN-NING MODELS...

HISTORICAL SURVEY OF URBAN PLANNING MODELS: PAGES 23-31.

URBAN NATURE IN METROBASEL: PAGES 32-35

... AND A DESCRIPTION OF WHAT WE CALL 'URBAN NATURE'. MY COLLEAGUE FUMIKO WILL HELP OUT THERE.

... AND THEN WE'LL WRAP UP THE INTRODUCTION WITH A LOOK AT ECONOMIC FACTORS IN THE REGION. THE GUEST SPEAKER WILL BE CHRISTOPH KOELLREUTER.

ECONOMIC FACTORS IN THE REGION: PAGES 36-43

SO, LET'S GET STARTED...

13

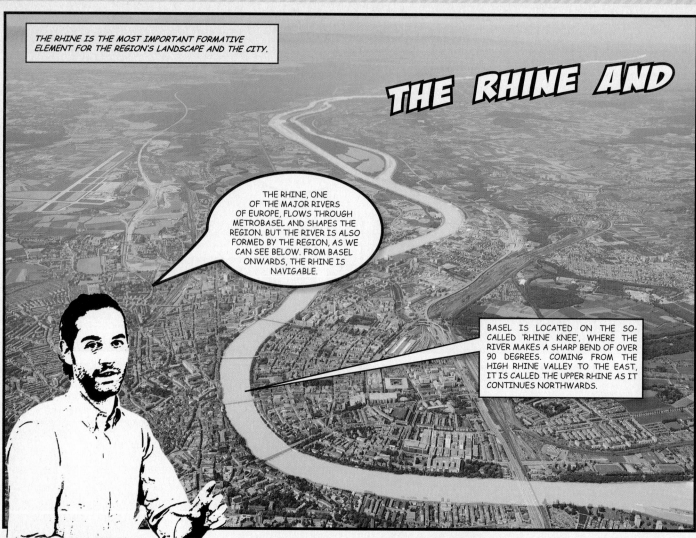

THE RHINE IS THE MOST IMPORTANT FORMATIVE ELEMENT FOR THE REGION'S LANDSCAPE AND THE CITY.

THE RHINE AND

THE RHINE, ONE OF THE MAJOR RIVERS OF EUROPE, FLOWS THROUGH METROBASEL AND SHAPES THE REGION. BUT THE RIVER IS ALSO FORMED BY THE REGION, AS WE CAN SEE BELOW. FROM BASEL ONWARDS, THE RHINE IS NAVIGABLE.

BASEL IS LOCATED ON THE SO-CALLED 'RHINE KNEE', WHERE THE RIVER MAKES A SHARP BEND OF OVER 90 DEGREES. COMING FROM THE HIGH RHINE VALLEY TO THE EAST, IT IS CALLED THE UPPER RHINE AS IT CONTINUES NORTHWARDS.

THE RHINE BEFORE THE STRAIGHTENING OF THE RIVERBED, C.MID-19TH CENTURY.

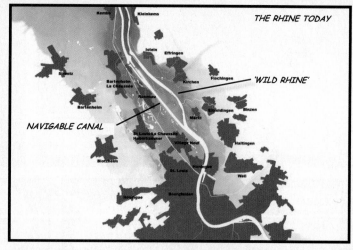

THE RHINE TODAY

'WILD RHINE'

NAVIGABLE CANAL

THE RHINE USED TO LOOK DIFFERENT... IT HAD MANY SIDE BRANCHES AND PASTURES, AND WAS ROMANTIC TO BEHOLD. THE RIVER MEANDERED CONSIDERABLY.

TODAY, THE COURSE OF THE RHINE HAS BEEN STRAIGHTENED AND DIVIDED INTO A NAVIGABLE BRANCH, WHICH HAS THE APPEARANCE OF A HIGHWAY, AND THE 'WILD RHINE', WHICH FLOWS SLIGHTLY TO THE EAST.

THIS IS THE RHINE AS IT PASSES THROUGH THE CITY CENTER OF BASEL. IN THE FOREGROUND, YOU CAN SEE THE MITTLERE BRÜCKE.

THE OTHER ESSENTIAL FORMATIVE ELEMENTS THAT GIVE SHAPE TO THE REGION ARE THE THREE MAJOR TOPOGRAPHICAL REGIONS THAT CONVERGE ON BASEL...

THE TOPOGRAPHIC REGIONS

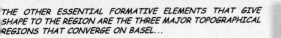

THE SUNDGAU

THE SUNDGAU IS PART OF ALSACE AND USED TO BE THE 'BREAD-BASKET OF BASEL'.

THE BLACK FOREST

THE BLACK FOREST IS A DENSELY WOODED MOUNTAIN RANGE IN SOUTHWESTERN GERMANY.

THE JURA

THE JURA IS A MOUNTAIN RANGE NORTHWEST OF THE ALPS STRETCHING FROM SWITZERLAND TO FRANCE.

FIND OUT MORE ABOUT THE TOPOGRAPHICAL ZONES IN THE CHAPTER ON 'RECREATION', PAGE 207...

... THE SUNDGAU ...

... BLACK FOREST...

THIS CONSTELLATION OF THREE DIFFERENT LANDSCAPE FORMATIONS COMING TOGETHER AT ONE POINT IS UNIQUE IN EUROPE AND IS PART OF THE REGION'S GREAT APPEAL.

AND THE JURA

15

SOME OF THE EARLIEST EVIDENCE OF SETTLEMENT IN THE AREA AROUND THE MODERN-DAY CITY WAS LEFT BY THE CELTS. THE CELTS WERE AN ANCIENT PEOPLE LIVING IN CENTRAL EUROPE DURING THE IRON AGE, ABOUT 2500 YEARS AGO. EVEN THOUGH THEY DID NOT FORM A CONTIGUOUS ETHNIC-ITY, THEY CAN NEVERTHE-LESS BE REGARDED AS THE FIRST EUROPEAN CULTURAL GROUP BECAUSE OF THEIR COMMON CULTURE AND LANGUAGE.

THE CELTS

CELTIC SETTLEMENT AREA AROUND 500 B.C. ...

ABOUT 2500 YEARS AGO, THE CELTS SETTLED IN TWO LOCATIONS ON THE TERRITORY OF MODERN-DAY BASEL. WHERE THE BIRSIG RIVER FLOWS INTO THE RHINE, THE RHINE WAS PROBABLY SHALLOW AND FEA-TURED SEVERAL IS-LANDS THAT MADE IT EASY TO CROSS OVER AND CREATED NATURAL BERTHS FOR BOATS. THE SECOND SETTLE-MENT WAS ON THE HILL OVERLOOKING THE RHINE KNEE, WHICH FORMED A GOOD STRATEGIC POSITION.

THE HISTORY OF METROBASEL

OK, LET ME START BY TELLING YOU A LITTLE ABOUT THE HISTORY OF THE REGION AND THE CITY...

... AND THE REGION SURROUNDING BASEL WAS A CENTRAL LOCATION FOR THE CELTS...

'GAS FACTORY'

'MÜNSTER HILL'

THERE HAVE BEEN HUMAN SETTLEMENTS IN THE REGION OF MODERN-DAY METROBASEL FOR SEVERAL THOUSANDS OF YEARS.

THE RHINE FLOWS FROM THE EAST OUT OF THE NARROW HIGH RHINE VALLEY, ARCHING AROUND BEFORE IT ENTERS THE BROADER UPPER RHINE RIFT. AT THIS POINT, THREE MINOR RIVERS FEED INTO THE RHINE - THE WIESE, THE BIRS, AND THE BIRSIG - CREATING NATURAL BERTHS FOR SHIPPING. THE 'KNEE OF THE RHINE' IS OVERLOOKED BY A HILL FROM WHICH THE ENTIRE REGION CAN BE SURVEYED. THIS WAS AN IDEAL PLACE FOR BUILDING A SETTLEMENT.

THE SIGNIFICANCE OF THIS PLACE IS ALSO HIGHLIGHTED BY THE POSITION OF DISTINCTIVE HILLTOPS: THE SO-CALLED BELCHENS, WHOSE LOCATIONS CORRESPOND TO CERTAIN POSITIONS OF THE SUN (SEE PAGE 206)

BUT THE CELTS DID NOT ONLY SETTLE IN THE ARC OF THE RHINE BECAUSE OF LOCAL ADVANTAGES ON THE GROUND. THE PLACE ALSO HAD A TRANSCENDENT MEANING FOR THEM, AS IT IS LINKED INTO A NETWORK OF ASTRONOMICAL AND GEOMETRIC SIGNIFICANCE.

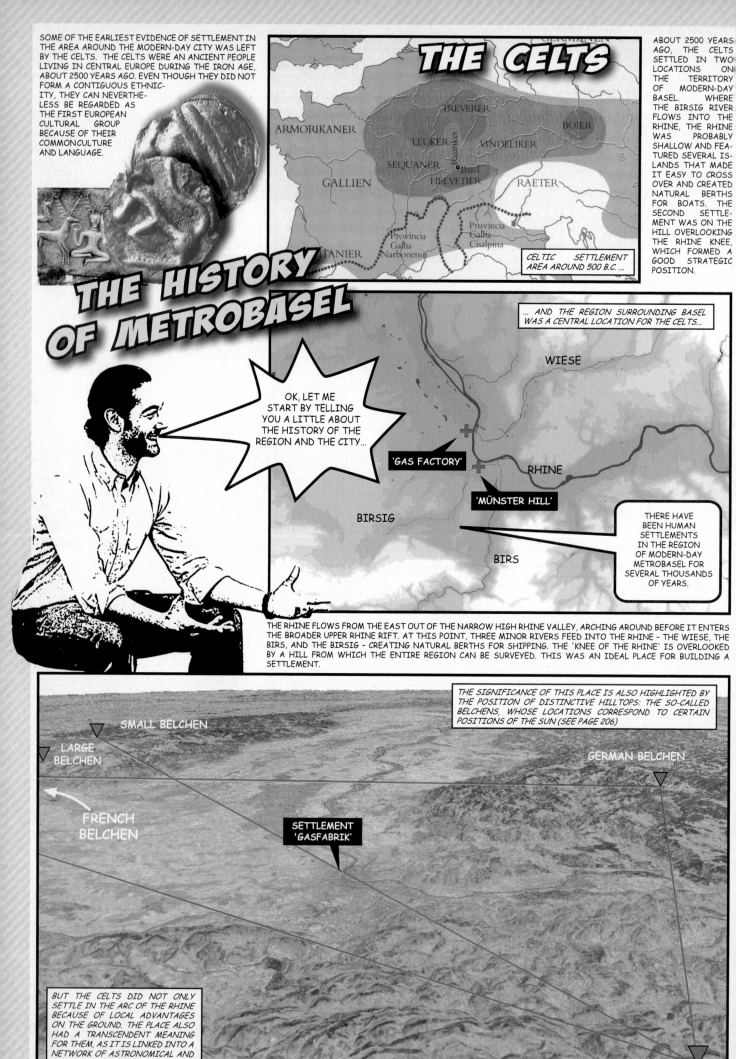

SMALL BELCHEN

LARGE BELCHEN

FRENCH BELCHEN

GERMAN BELCHEN

SETTLEMENT 'GASFABRIK'

SWISS BELCHEN

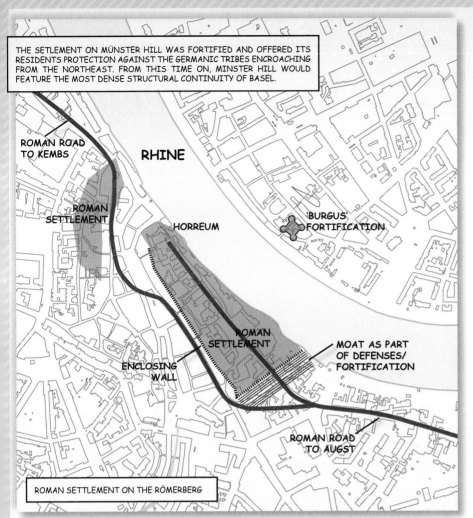

THE SETLEMENT ON MÜNSTER HILL WAS FORTIFIED AND OFFERED ITS RESIDENTS PROTECTION AGAINST THE GERMANIC TRIBES ENCROACHING FROM THE NORTHEAST. FROM THIS TIME ON, MINSTER HILL WOULD FEATURE THE MOST DENSE STRUCTURAL CONTINUITY OF BASEL.

ROMAN ROAD TO KEMBS

RHINE

ROMAN SETTLEMENT

HORREUM

'BURGUS' FORTIFICATION

ROMAN SETTLEMENT

ENCLOSING WALL

MOAT AS PART OF DEFENSES/ FORTIFICATION

ROMAN ROAD TO AUGST

ROMAN SETTLEMENT ON THE RÖMERBERG

THE ROMANS

THE ROMANS CAME UP THE RHINE WITH A LARGE ARMY IN 15 B.C. AND CONQUERED THE CELTIC REGION OF BASEL. THEY CONSTRUCTED A ROMAN FORT ON MINSTER HILL. CLEARLY, THE ROMANS, TOO, IMMEDIATELY SAW THE STRATEGIC VALUE OF THIS ELEVATION ON THE RIVERBANK. THEIR MILITARY PRESENCE ALLOWED THEM TO GO ON FORAYS NORTHWARDS TO FIGHT AGAINST THE GERMANS. BASEL – OR 'ROBUR', AS THE ROMANS CALLED IT – THUS HAD WARLIKE ORIGINS. IT WAS NEITHER A RESIDENTIAL CITY NOR A CIVIC COMMUNITY IN THE SENSE OF THE LATIN 'CIVIS' WITH A LARGE CIVILIAN POPULATION.

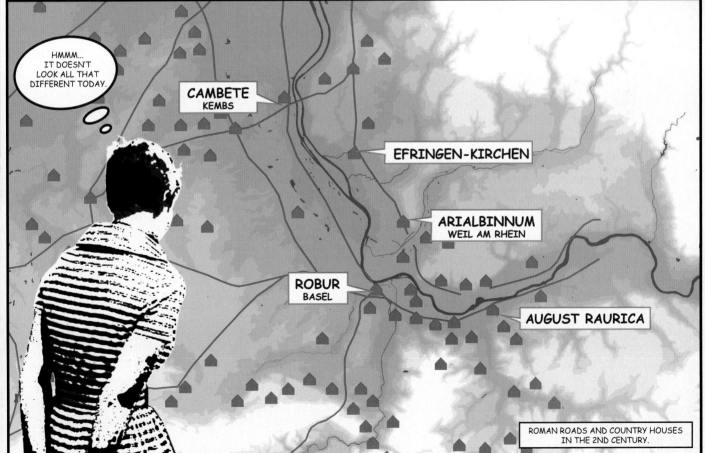

HMMM... IT DOESN'T LOOK ALL THAT DIFFERENT TODAY.

CAMBETE
KEMBS

EFRINGEN-KIRCHEN

ARIALBINNUM
WEIL AM RHEIN

ROBUR
BASEL

AUGUST RAURICA

ROMAN ROADS AND COUNTRY HOUSES IN THE 2ND CENTURY.

IN ADDITION TO SETTLING IN 'ROBUR', AS BASEL WAS THEN CALLED, THE ROMANS ALSO FOUNDED SEVERAL OTHER SETTLEMENTS AND TOWNS. INDEED BASEL WAS NOT THE MOST IMPORTANT ROMAN TOWN IN THE REGION. DUE TO ITS ADVANTAGEOUS SITUATION, IT SERVED INSTEAD AS A MILITARY BASE, WHILE THE 'CIVILIAN' POPULATION LIVED IN ARIALBINNUM (WEIL AM RHEIN) OR EFRINGEN-KIRCHEN, BUT MAINLY IN AUGUSTA RAURICA. THIS WAS THE MAIN TOWN IN THE REGION, AN ELABORATELY DESIGNED AND DEVELOPED ROMAN CITY.

BUT OUTSIDE OF THE ROMAN CITIES WITH THEIR URBAN STRUCTURES, A LARGE PART OF THE POPULATION LIVED IN COUNTRY HOUSES AND VILLAS SPREAD OUT ACROSS THE ENTIRE REGION. BY THE STANDARDS OF THE TIME, THE REGION WAS DENSELY POPULATED. IT WAS CONNECTED BY A WELL-DEVELOPED SYSTEM OF ROADS AND TRADE ROUTES THAT NOT ONLY ALLOWED TRAVEL IN THE IMMEDIATE VICINITY, BUT CONNECTED THE REGION TO MORE DISTANT PLACES. ESSENTIALLY, THE ROMANS THUS DEVELOPED A CONTIGUOUS METROPOLITAN REGION, ALMOST A KIND OF METROBASEL AVANT LA LETTRE.

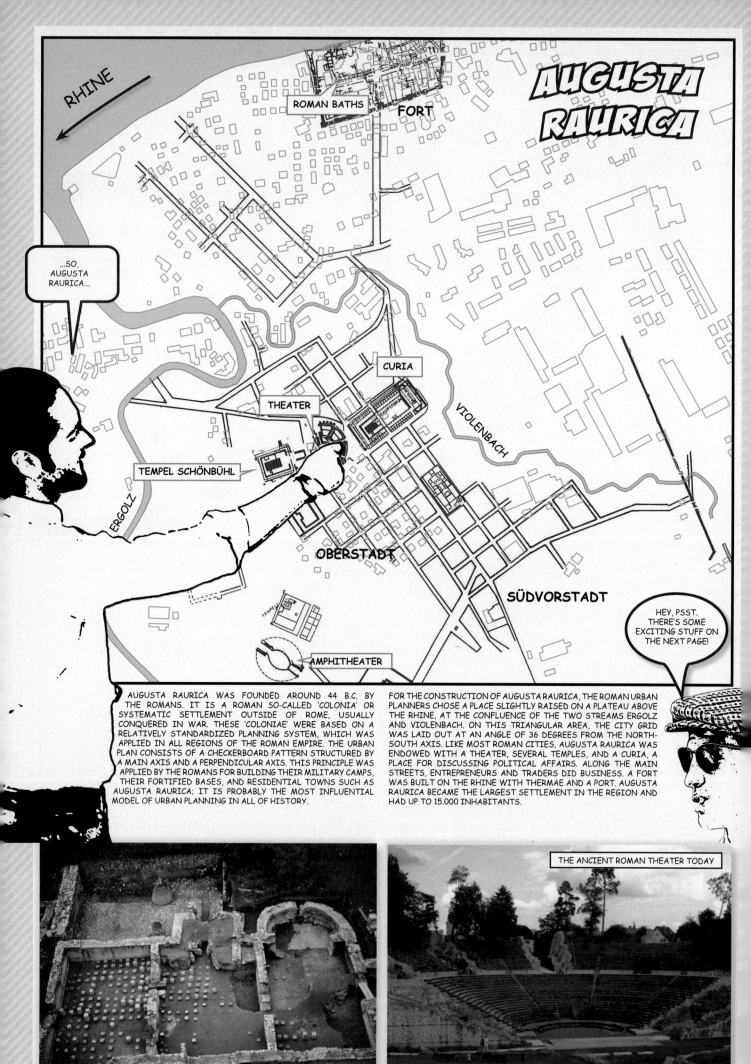

AUGUSTA RAURICA

RHINE

ROMAN BATHS

FORT

...SO, AUGUSTA RAURICA...

CURIA

THEATER

VIOLENBACH

TEMPEL SCHÖNBÜHL

ERGOLZ

OBERSTADT

SÜDVORSTADT

HEY, PSST. THERE'S SOME EXCITING STUFF ON THE NEXT PAGE!

AMPHITHEATER

AUGUSTA RAURICA WAS FOUNDED AROUND 44 B.C. BY THE ROMANS. IT IS A ROMAN SO-CALLED 'COLONIA' OR SYSTEMATIC SETTLEMENT OUTSIDE OF ROME, USUALLY CONQUERED IN WAR. THESE 'COLONIAE' WERE BASED ON A RELATIVELY STANDARDIZED PLANNING SYSTEM, WHICH WAS APPLIED IN ALL REGIONS OF THE ROMAN EMPIRE. THE URBAN PLAN CONSISTS OF A CHECKERBOARD PATTERN STRUCTURED BY A MAIN AXIS AND A PERPENDICULAR AXIS. THIS PRINCIPLE WAS APPLIED BY THE ROMANS FOR BUILDING THEIR MILITARY CAMPS, THEIR FORTIFIED BASES, AND RESIDENTIAL TOWNS SUCH AS AUGUSTA RAURICA; IT IS PROBABLY THE MOST INFLUENTIAL MODEL OF URBAN PLANNING IN ALL OF HISTORY.

FOR THE CONSTRUCTION OF AUGUSTA RAURICA, THE ROMAN URBAN PLANNERS CHOSE A PLACE SLIGHTLY RAISED ON A PLATEAU ABOVE THE RHINE, AT THE CONFLUENCE OF THE TWO STREAMS ERGOLZ AND VIOLENBACH. ON THIS TRIANGULAR AREA, THE CITY GRID WAS LAID OUT AT AN ANGLE OF 36 DEGREES FROM THE NORTH-SOUTH AXIS. LIKE MOST ROMAN CITIES, AUGUSTA RAURICA WAS ENDOWED WITH A THEATER, SEVERAL TEMPLES, AND A CURIA, A PLACE FOR DISCUSSING POLITICAL AFFAIRS. ALONG THE MAIN STREETS, ENTREPRENEURS AND TRADERS DID BUSINESS. A FORT WAS BUILT ON THE RHINE WITH THERMAE AND A PORT. AUGUSTA RAURICA BECAME THE LARGEST SETTLEMENT IN THE REGION AND HAD UP TO 15.000 INHABITANTS.

THE ANCIENT ROMAN THEATER TODAY

CONTEMPORARY EXCAVATIONS OF THE ROMAN BATHS AT THE FORT

THE DARK AGES IN BASEL

ONLY VERY LITTLE IS KNOWN ABOUT THE TIME BETWEEN THE DEPARTURE OF THE ROMANS AND THE FOUNDATION OF THE 'HOLY ROMAN EMPIRE' IN THE 10TH CENTURY. THIS IS A MURKY PERIOD IN BASEL'S HISTORY.

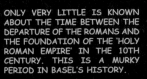

CHRISTIANIZATION BEGAN IN THE 4TH CENTURY. THE EARLIEST EVIDENCE IS A GRAVESTONE WITH CHRISTIAN SYMBOLS FOUND DURING EXCAVATIONS.

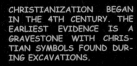

WE ARE TOLD THAT THE FIRST BISHOP WAS IUSTINIANUS RAURICORUM, BUT HE PROBABLY LIVED IN AUGUSTA RAURICA. BASEL WAS MOST LIKELY JUST A MINOR APPENDAGE OF AUGST AT THE TIME.

AT SOME POINT IN THE 5TH CENTURY, THE ALAMANNI ENTERED INTO THE REGION FROM THE NORTH. NOT MANY DETAILS ARE KNOWN ABOUT THIS PERIOD, SINCE THERE ARE ONLY FEW ARCHAEOLOGICAL FINDS. IN 456, THE POET APOLLINARIS COMPOSED THIS VERSE:

YOU DRANK THE RHINE, FEROCIOUS ALAMAN, ON THE ROMAN RIVERBANK, AND ON BOTH SIDES YOU PROUDLY DWELT, ON THE ONE SHORE A CITIZEN, ON THE OTHER A VICTOR.

AT THE TIME, THE ALAMANNI WERE FIGHTING AGAINST THE ROMANI, A TRIBE SETTLING IN THE FRENCH-SPEAKING PART OF SWITZERLAND THAT IS TODAY NAMED 'ROMANDY' AFTER THEM; AND IN MODERN-DAY BURGUNDY.

WHILE THE RHINE AT BASEL MARKED THE BORDER BETWEEN TWO EMPIRES, THE POPULATION WAS INTERMINGLED ACROSS THE REGION.

IN THE 6TH CENTURY, THE ERA OF FRANKISH RULE IN THE REGION BEGAN. HERE, TOO, IMPORTANT ASPECTS REMAIN OBSCURE. THE FRANKISH EMPIRE WAS RULED BY CLOVIS, THE HEAD OF THE MEROVINGIAN DYNASTY.

CLOVIS I,
481-511

THERE ARE VERY FEW RELICS, REFERENCES IN DOCUMENTS, OR REPORTS RELATING TO THE FIRST CENTURY OF THE FRANKISH ERA IN BASEL. WE KNOW VERY LITTLE ABOUT THAT PERIOD.

THE MOST IMPORTANT CHANGE AS FAR AS BASEL'S URBAN DEVELOPMENT IS CONCERNED WAS THE CREATION OF THE DIOCESE OF BASEL. FOR UNKNOWN REASONS, A BISHOP DECIDED AROUND 740 TO MOVE HIS SEAT FROM AUGST TO BASEL. THIS WAS THE BEGINNING OF THE RISE OF THE CITY.

BISHOP OF BASEL,
NAME UNKNOWN
(POSSIBLY WALAUS),
C. 8TH CENTURY

HAITO IS THE FIRST BISHOP OF BASEL ABOUT WHOM MORE IS KNOWN. HE ORDERED THE BUILDING OF THE FIRST MINSTER, THE PRE-PREDECESSOR OF THE CURRENT STRUCTURE. THUS HAITO USED URBAN CONSTRUCTION TO CONSOLIDATE POWER ON MINSTER HILL.

BISHOP HAITO
OF BASEL,
763-836

DURING THIS PERIOD, BASEL CONSISTED OF SEVERAL INDIVIDUAL SETTLEMENTS. NO CONTIGUOUS URBAN FABRIC HAD DEVELOPED YET. RATHER, THE TOWN WAS MADE UP OF VARIOUS MORE OR LESS CLOSELY CONNECTED 'EPICENTERS'*. USUALLY, SUCH HOMESTEADS OR CLUSTERS OF HOUSES WERE OWNED BY INDIVIDUAL FAMILIES.

THESE EARLY MEDIEVAL POLYCENTRIC TOWNS ARE CALLED 'OTTONIAN TOWNS'. SEE:
ERICH HERZOG: DIE OTTONISCHE STADT, BERLIN, 1958

THE DEVELOPMENT OF THE CITY FORTIFICATIONS*

THE MIDDLE AGES

*SEE ALSO THE BOOK 'MAUERN, SCHANZEN, TORE' BY ANDREAS FISCHER, CHRISTOPH MERIAN VERLAG, 2007, FOR MORE INFORMATION ON THIS TOPIC.

CITY WALL BUILT BY BISHOP BURKHARD, C.1080-1090

INTERIOR CITY WALL, C. 1250 (?)

KLEINBASEL 13TH CENTURY

THE ANCIENT CITY CENTER, 1ST CENTURY B.C.-12TH CENTURY

RHINE

EXTERIOR CITY WALL, MID-14TH CENTURY

ST ALBAN'S MONASTERY, 11TH CENTURY

FROM THE 11TH CENTURY ON, BASEL WAS SURROUNDED BY A CITY WALL. THE FIRST WALL AROUND TODAY'S OLD TOWN WAS BUILT BY BISHOP BURKHARD.

THIS IS THE OLDEST KNOWN DEPICTION OF BASEL.* IT SHOWS THE EARLY MEDIEVAL OLD TOWN AND KLEINBASEL SURROUNDED BY CITY WALLS AND CONNECTED BY THE MITTLERE BRÜCKE.

THREE MEDIEVAL CITY WALLS WERE CONSTRUCTED DURING THE HISTORY OF GROSS-BASEL: THE OLDEST, BUILT BY BURKHARD, WAS ONLY RECENTLY DISCOVERED. IT RAN JUST INSIDE THE SO-CALLED 'INTERIOR CITY WALL', WHICH WAS BUILT IN THE MID-13TH CENTURY. WHEN BASEL LATER BEGAN TO EXPAND, THE EXTERIOR WALL WAS BUILT FOLLOWING THE DISASTROUS EARTHQUAKE OF 1365.

BURKHARD'S CITY WALL AND MOAT

SQUARE DEFENSIVE TOWER, C. 1200

INTERIOR CITY WALL WITH BATTLEMENT, PARAPETS, AND RAMPS FOR THE CITY GUARD.

DIE ALTE VND ERSTE STAT BASEL

*THIS IS AN 18TH-CENTURY WOODCUT OF A MUCH OLDER DRAWING THAT CLAIMS TO DEPICT BASEL IN THE 13TH CENTURY. HOWEVER, THERE ARE SOME INCONSISTENCIES: THE MÜNSTER IS SHOWN AS IT APPEARED BEFORE THE 1356 EARTHQUAKE, BUT THE CHAPEL ON MITTLERE BRÜCKE WAS NOT BUILT UNTIL AFTER THE EARTHQUAKE.

THE EARTHQUAKE AND THE PLAGUE

THE GREAT EARTHQUAKE OF BASEL, 1356: HISTORY PAINTING BY ARTIST KARL JAUSLIN (1842-1904) OF BASEL-COUNTRY.

IN THE MIDDLE OF THE 14TH CENTURY, BASEL WAS SEVERLY AFFLICTED BY TWO CATASTROPHES: THE PLAGUE AND A MASSIVE EARTHQUAKE. THE QUAKE, WHICH OCCURRED NEAR BASEL ON 18 OCTOBER 1356, IS THE WORST EVER IN THE RECORDED HISTORY OF EUROPE. IT DESTROYED LARGE PARTS OF THE CITY, AND HUNDREDS OF CITIZENS PERISHED IN THE SUBSEQUENT FIRE.

AT THE SAME TIME, THE PLAGUE SWEPT THROUGH THE CITY AND KILLED A LARGE PART OF THE POPULATION. DURING THIS TIME, AS DEATH BECAME COMMONPLACE, A PICTURE WAS PAINTED IN A MONASTERY JUST OUTSIDE THE CITY GATES DEPICTING THESE EVENTS: THE DANCE OF DEATH. THIS IS ALSO THE LOCATION OF THE GRAVEYARD WHERE MANY PLAGUE VICTIMS WERE BURIED. EVEN TODAY, THE PLACE IS STILL NAMED FOR THE PICTURE AND THE ASSOCIATED EVENTS.

THE PLAGUE AND ESPECIALLY THE EARTHQUAKE ARE TWO TRAGIC EVENTS THAT LED TO RECONSTRUCTION OF THE CITY* AND THEREFORE INDIRECTLY HELPED TO SHAPE IT.

*AS EXPLAINED ON THE PREVIOUS PAGE, FOR EXAMPLE, THE EXTERIOR CITY WALL WAS BUILT AS PART OF RECONSTRUCTION EFFORTS AFTER THE EARTHQUAKE.

DEVELOPMENT OF THE MEDIEVAL CITY

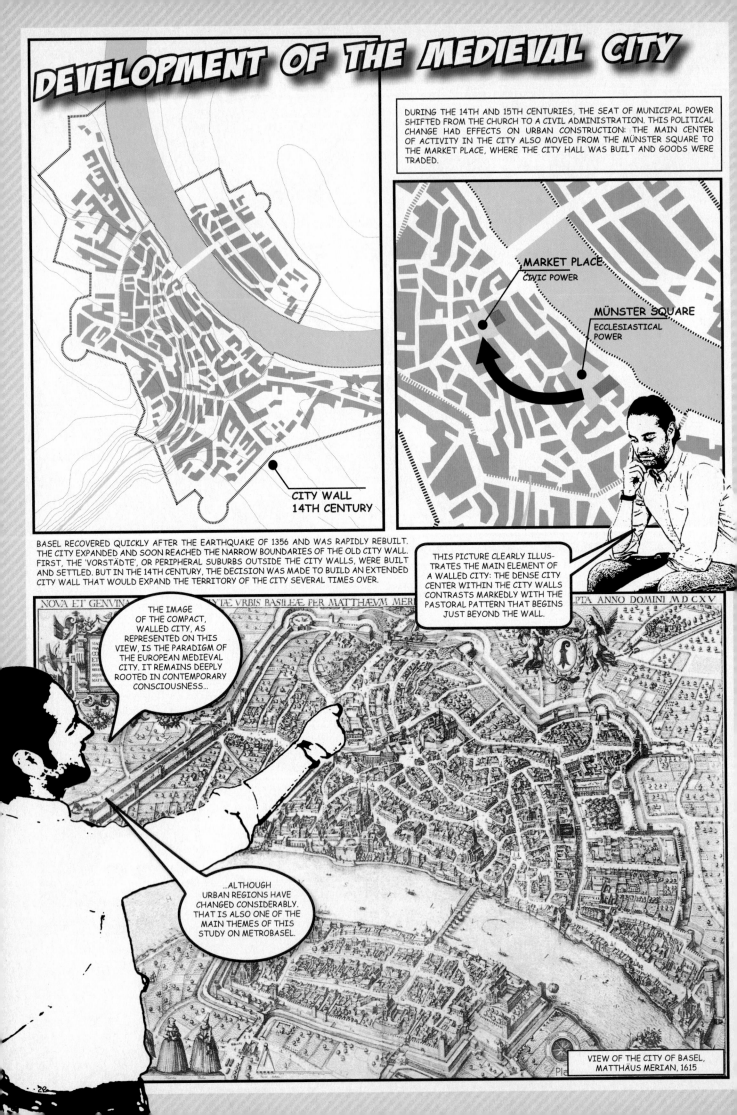

DURING THE 14TH AND 15TH CENTURIES, THE SEAT OF MUNICIPAL POWER SHIFTED FROM THE CHURCH TO A CIVIL ADMINISTRATION. THIS POLITICAL CHANGE HAD EFFECTS ON URBAN CONSTRUCTION: THE MAIN CENTER OF ACTIVITY IN THE CITY ALSO MOVED FROM THE MÜNSTER SQUARE TO THE MARKET PLACE, WHERE THE CITY HALL WAS BUILT AND GOODS WERE TRADED.

CITY WALL 14TH CENTURY

MARKET PLACE
CIVIC POWER

MÜNSTER SQUARE
ECCLESIASTICAL POWER

BASEL RECOVERED QUICKLY AFTER THE EARTHQUAKE OF 1356 AND WAS RAPIDLY REBUILT. THE CITY EXPANDED AND SOON REACHED THE NARROW BOUNDARIES OF THE OLD CITY WALL. FIRST, THE 'VORSTÄDTE', OR PERIPHERAL SUBURBS OUTSIDE THE CITY WALLS, WERE BUILT AND SETTLED. BUT IN THE 14TH CENTURY, THE DECISION WAS MADE TO BUILD AN EXTENDED CITY WALL THAT WOULD EXPAND THE TERRITORY OF THE CITY SEVERAL TIMES OVER.

THIS PICTURE CLEARLY ILLUS-TRATES THE MAIN ELEMENT OF A WALLED CITY: THE DENSE CITY CENTER WITHIN THE CITY WALLS CONTRASTS MARKEDLY WITH THE PASTORAL PATTERN THAT BEGINS JUST BEYOND THE WALL.

THE IMAGE OF THE COMPACT, WALLED CITY, AS REPRESENTED ON THIS VIEW, IS THE PARADIGM OF THE EUROPEAN MEDIEVAL CITY. IT REMAINS DEEPLY ROOTED IN CONTEMPORARY CONSCIOUSNESS...

...ALTHOUGH URBAN REGIONS HAVE CHANGED CONSIDERABLY. THAT IS ALSO ONE OF THE MAIN THEMES OF THIS STUDY ON METROBASEL.

VIEW OF THE CITY OF BASEL, MATTHÄUS MERIAN, 1615

THE MARING PLAN

AT THE BEGINNING OF THE 19TH CENTURY, IT BECAME IN-CREASINGLY CLEAR THAT THE CITY WALL WAS OBSTRUCTING THE DEVELOPMENT OF THE CITY. PEOPLE STARTED THINKING ABOUT WAYS IN WHICH THE CITY COULD DEVELOP WITH-OUT THE WALLS. IN 1857, LUDWIG MARING PRESENTED A PLAN FOR BASEL THAT ENVISIONED A CIRCULAR EXPANSION AROUND THE MEDIEVAL CORE CITY BASED ON A CLASSICIST STRUCTURE.
THIS PLAN EMBODIED A *F U N D A M E N T A L L Y* NEW CON-CEPT OF WHAT CONSTITUTES A CITY. INSTEAD OF LETTING THE NATURAL TOPOGRAPHY SHAPE THE CITY, AS HAD BEEN THE CASE IN THE MIDDLE AGES, THE CITY WAS NOW TO GIVE SHAPE TO A NEW 'ENVIRONMENT'.

IT WAS ALSO THE BEGINNING OF WHAT COULD BE CALLED THE 'GENERIC' OR 'UNSPECIFIC' CITY, SINCE DURING THAT TIME, MANY EUROPEAN CITIES WERE CONSIDERING SIMILAR URBAN EXPANSION PLANS.

GENERALPLAN DER

STADT BASEL

VON
L. MARING, ARCHITEKT

1857

AS INFLUENTIAL AS THE MARING PLAN WAS, ONLY VERY LITTLE OF IT WAS REALIZED. IN FACT, ONLY TWO ELEMENTS: THE BARRACKS AND THE AREA SURROUNDING THE LOCATION OF THE MODERN-DAY THEATER. MAYBE THIS URBAN MODEL WAS TOO RADICAL FOR A BOURGEOIS SOCIETY?

THE 'BARRACKS' ON THE RHINE, BUILT ACCORD-ING TO THE PLANS OF LUDWIG MARING

IT'S REALLY REMARKABLE – IMAGINE, UNTIL 150 YEARS AGO, BASEL WAS LIMITED TO THE AREA MARKED BY THE OLD CITY WALL. IT MUST HAVE GROWN REALLY QUICKLY AFTERWARDS.

THE MEDIEVAL CITY WALL WAS ONLY DISMANTLED STARTING IN 1859. UNTIL THEN, ALMOST ALL OF BASEL'S BUILDINGS HAD BEEN WITHIN THE WALLS. THUS, THE FIRST NEW QUARTERS WERE CONSTRUCTED IN THE SECOND HALF OF THE 19TH CENTURY ALONG THE COURSE OF THE EARLIER BOUNDARY WALL.

THIS PHASE WAS FOLLOWED SEAMLESSLY BY THE EARLY 20TH CENTURY, WHICH WAS SHAPED MORE BY INDUSTRIALIZATION. DURING THIS PERIOD, CLASSICIST IDEAS WERE REALIZED BASED ON A RIGOROUS, OFTEN ORTHOGONAL URBAN GRID.

...AND EARLY 20TH CENTURY

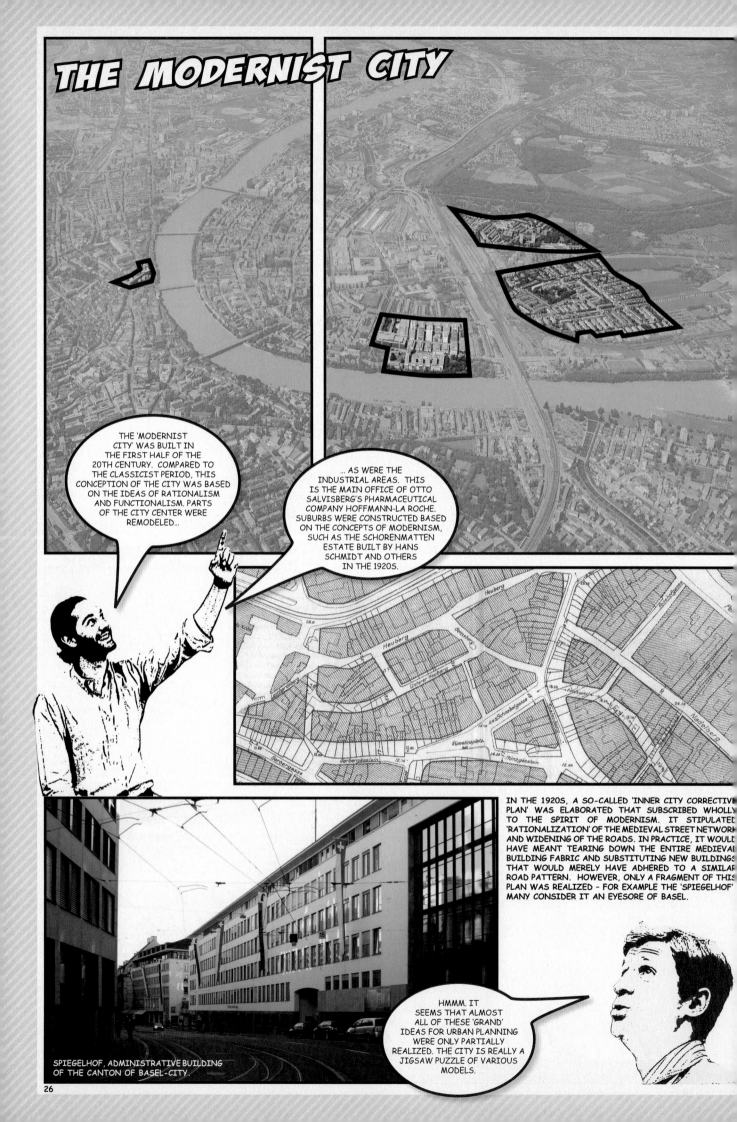

THE MODERNIST CITY

THE 'MODERNIST CITY' WAS BUILT IN THE FIRST HALF OF THE 20TH CENTURY. COMPARED TO THE CLASSICIST PERIOD, THIS CONCEPTION OF THE CITY WAS BASED ON THE IDEAS OF RATIONALISM AND FUNCTIONALISM. PARTS OF THE CITY CENTER WERE REMODELED...

... AS WERE THE INDUSTRIAL AREAS. THIS IS THE MAIN OFFICE OF OTTO SALVISBERG'S PHARMACEUTICAL COMPANY HOFFMANN-LA ROCHE. SUBURBS WERE CONSTRUCTED BASED ON THE CONCEPTS OF MODERNISM, SUCH AS THE SCHORENMATTEN ESTATE BUILT BY HANS SCHMIDT AND OTHERS IN THE 1920S.

IN THE 1920S, A SO-CALLED 'INNER CITY CORRECTIVE PLAN' WAS ELABORATED THAT SUBSCRIBED WHOLLY TO THE SPIRIT OF MODERNISM. IT STIPULATED 'RATIONALIZATION' OF THE MEDIEVAL STREET NETWORK AND WIDENING OF THE ROADS. IN PRACTICE, IT WOULD HAVE MEANT TEARING DOWN THE ENTIRE MEDIEVAL BUILDING FABRIC AND SUBSTITUTING NEW BUILDINGS THAT WOULD MERELY HAVE ADHERED TO A SIMILAR ROAD PATTERN. HOWEVER, ONLY A FRAGMENT OF THIS PLAN WAS REALIZED - FOR EXAMPLE THE 'SPIEGELHOF'. MANY CONSIDER IT AN EYESORE OF BASEL.

HMMM. IT SEEMS THAT ALMOST ALL OF THESE 'GRAND' IDEAS FOR URBAN PLANNING WERE ONLY PARTIALLY REALIZED. THE CITY IS REALLY A JIGSAW PUZZLE OF VARIOUS MODELS.

SPIEGELHOF, ADMINISTRATIVE BUILDING OF THE CANTON OF BASEL-CITY.

THE 'POST-WAR' ERA*

*ACTUALLY, IT IS PARADOXICAL TO SPEAK OF A POST-WAR ERA IN BASEL, SINCE THE CITY WAS HARDLY INVOLVED IN WORLD WAR II. NEVERTHELESS, THE REGION WAS AFFECTED BY MANY OF THE TRENDS THAT ALSO SHAPED URBAN DEVELOPMENT IN GERMANY, FRANCE, AND OTHER EUROPEAN COUNTRIES FROM THE 1950S TO THE 1970S.

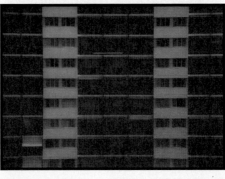

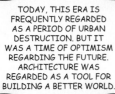

TODAY, THIS ERA IS FREQUENTLY REGARDED AS A PERIOD OF URBAN DESTRUCTION. BUT IT WAS A TIME OF OPTIMISM REGARDING THE FUTURE. ARCHITECTURE WAS REGARDED AS A TOOL FOR BUILDING A BETTER WORLD.

IN THE POST-WAR PERIOD, THE ORGANICALLY GROWN URBAN STRUCTURES EXPERIENCED SEVERE INTRUSION.

...WE COULD USE SOME OF THAT BOLDNESS AGAIN TODAY...

THE HEUWAAGE VIADUCT IS PART OF A TRAFFIC PROJECT PLANNED IN THE 1960S TO BUILD A 'CITY RING' AROUND THE CENTER. RESISTANCE TO THE HIGHLY INVASIVE PROJECT ONLY AROSE AT A LATE STAGE AND WAS LARGELY UNSUCCESSFUL. TODAY, THE VIADUCT IS ONE OF THE MOST IMPORTANT THOROUGHFARES OF THE CITY. IN MOST EUROPEAN CITIES AT THE TIME, SIMILAR PROJECTS WERE REALIZED, MOST OF WHICH ARE TODAY REGARDED AS ARCHITECTURAL ABOMINATIONS.

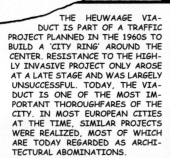

CONSTRUCTION OF HEUWAAGE VIADUCT, C. 1967

27

THE SUBURBAN CITY

DURING THE 1970S, JUST AS RESISTANCE TO POSTWAR ARCHITECTURE HAD REACHED ITS FIRST APEX, A PROCESS KNOWN AS 'SUBURBANIZATION' SET IN: A CONSIDERABLE PART OF THE POPULATION MOVED INTO NEW RESIDENTIAL AREAS OUTSIDE OF THE CITY PROPER. THE CITY WAS MASSIVELY EXPANDED IN TERMS OF AREA SIZE.

YOUNG FAMILIES IN PARTICULAR MOVED OUT INTO THE COUNTRYSIDE, WHERE THEY COULD AFFORD MORE SPACE AND A GARDEN AND ALLOW THEIR CHILDREN TO PLAY OUTSIDE SAFELY.

THE DRAWBACK WAS URBAN SPRAWL IN THE SURROUNDING COUNTRY AND A LOSS OF TAX REVENUE FOR THE CITY CENTER.

THE CONTEMPORARY CITY

THE NOVARTIS CAMPUS IN THE NORTH OF BASEL NEAR THE FRENCH BORDER

ROBABLY THE MOST CHARACTERISTIC TRAIT OF THE CONTEMPORARY ITY IS THE FREQUENT EMERGENCE OF RESIDENTIAL CLUSTERS. THESE RE RELATIVELY LARGE-SCALE ESTATES THAT ARE DEVELOPED BY NVESTORS OR OWNERS. EXAMPLES INCLUDE THE PROJECTS OF THE NOVARTIS PHARMACOLOGICAL CORPORATION, THE EXHIBITION CENTER, R THE NEWLY DEVELOPED ERLENMATT AND DREISPITZ ESTATES.

THE NOVARTIS CAMPUS, WHICH IS CURRENTLY BEING BUILT IN THE NORTH OF BASEL, IS A DETACHED PART OF TOWN FEATURING HIGH-QUALITY ARCHITECTURE BY INTERNATIONAL STANDARDS. IT RAISES HIGHLY TOPICAL ISSUES ABOUT CONCEPTS OF OPEN VS. CLOSED CITIES.*

* OPEN / CLOSED, A STUDY OF URBAN CONSTRUCTION BY ETH STUDIO BASEL, NOV. 2007.

HMMMM... NOW WE'VE LOOKED AT ALL KINDS OF DIFFERENT URBAN MODELS. HOW DO THEY FIT TOGETHER...???

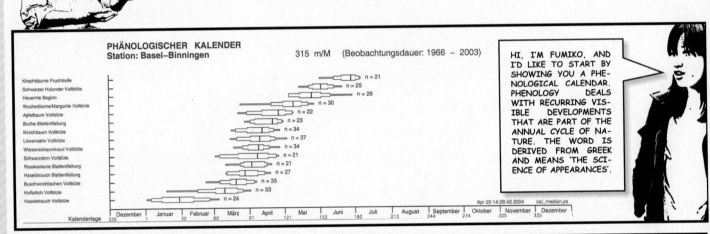

PETER SQUARE

FORMER CEMETERIES

CHURCH SQUARES

THE OLDEST PLANNED GREEN AREA OF BASEL WAS CREATED IN 1277 ON THE INSIDE OF THE CITY WALL. IT WAS SPECIFICALLY DESIGNED AS A SPORTS AND RECREATION AREA. TODAY, IT IS A CENTRAL SQUARE BESIDE THE MAIN UNIVERSITY BUILDING.

IN MEDIEVAL CITIES, CEMETERIES WERE OFTEN THE ONLY OPEN SPACES THAT WERE NOT USED COMMERCIALLY. LATER, MANY WERE DECONSECRATED AND REUSED AS PUBLIC GREEN SPACES.

IN ADDITION TO CEMETERIES, CHURCHES AND MONASTERIES USUALLY FEATURED OPEN PLANTED SPACES, SOME OF WHICH WERE EVEN PUT TO AGRICULTURAL USE. TODAY, THEY FREQUENTLY SERVE AS THE MAJOR PARKS OF A CITY.

THE 'CENTRAL PARK' OF METROBASEL

ALLOTMENT GARDENS

SPORTS AREAS AND ROADSIDE PLANTING

ALONG THE WIESE RIVER, WHICH FLOWS FROM THE BLACK FOREST TO THE RHINE, THERE IS A LARGE GREEN SPACE THAT STRADDLES GERMAN AND SWISS TERRITORY. WHY DON'T WE DEVELOP IT INTO A 'CENTRAL PARK' FOR METROBASEL WITH A LAKE AND ABUTTING RESIDENTIAL BUILDINGS?

THERE ARE ALLOTMENT GARDENS ALL ACROSS BASEL. THEY WERE ORIGINALLY INTENDED AS RECREATION AND RECOVERY SPACES FOR URBAN RESIDENTS, WHO COULD USE THEM TO PLANT THEIR OWN FOODSTUFFS. TODAY, THEY ARE FREQUENTLY USED FOR BARBECUES.

THE FIRST SPORTS AREAS WERE CONSTRUCTED IN THE 19TH CENTURY IN URBAN ENVIRONMENTS AS A NEW AWARENESS OF HYGIENE AND PHYSICAL TRAINING EMERGED. SOME OF THEM ARE STILL CLOSE TO PARKS CREATED AT THE SAME TIME.

19TH CENTURY PARKS

GREEN SPACES ALONG THE FORMER COURSE OF THE CITY WALL

GREEN SPACES ON RIVER BANKS

IN THE 19TH CENTURY, NOTIONS OF HYGIENE AND RECREATION EMERGED AND WERE COMBINED WITH URBAN PLANNING. AS THE LINK BETWEEN THE CITY AND THE PHYSICAL WELL-BEING OF ITS RESIDENTS BECAME CLEARER, PARKS AND ZOOS WERE PLANNED.

AT THE SAME TIME, IN MANY EUROPEAN CITIES, THE MEDIEVAL CITY WALLS WERE BEING DISMANTLED. NEW OPEN SPACES WERE CREATED CLOSE TO THE CITY CENTERS. THEY WERE FREQUENTLY PLANTED WITH GREENERY.

WHILE PREVIOUSLY, THE INDUSTRIAL ZONES ALONGSIDE RIVERS HAD BEEN POLLUTED AND DANGEROUS, IN THE 20TH CENTURY, RIVER BANKS WERE DISCOVERED AS PLACES FOR PEOPLE IN NEED OF RECREATION AND FLANEURS* .

AGRICULTURAL GREEN SPACES

MOOOOO... MMOOOO!!!!

*THE 'FLANEUR' (FROM FRENCH FLANER, TO STROLL) IS SOMEONE WHO, WHILE WALKING AROUND, OBSERVES IN SILENT ENJOYMENT. THE FLANEUR IS FREQUENTLY ENCOUNTERED AS A LITERARY FIGURE IN THE NOVEL OF THE CITY IN THE EARLY 20TH CENTURY, E.G. IN THE WORKS OF CHARLES BAUDELAIRE.

THESE ARE VARIOUS EXAMPLES OF URBAN NATURE THAT CAN BE FOUND IN THE METROBASEL REGION. OF COURSE, SUCH ZONES DO NOT ONLY EXIST IN BASEL, BUT ARE TYPCIAL OF EUROPEAN CITIES. THE BASEL REGION CAN BE CONSIDERED A TYPICAL EXAMPLE OF A EUROPEAN METROPOLITAN REGION.

WE SHOULD REGARD THESE AREAS OF URBAN NATURE NOT JUST AS RELICS BETWEEN BUILT AREAS, BUT PLAN THEM IN A PREMEDITATED MANER. CAN WE CONCEIVE OF URBAN DEVELOPMENT FOR GREEN AREAS, AND ELABORATE A TOOLBOX OF PLANNING INSTRUMENTS FOR URBAN NATURE THAT IS JUST AS SOPHISTICATED AS THE ONE DEVELOPED FOR THE BUILT ENVIRONMENT?

ALL ACROSS METROBASEL, EVEN IN VERY CENTRAL LOCATIONS, THERE ARE MANY AGRICULTURAL ZONES WHERE WINE AND GRAIN ARE CULTIVATED OR CATTLE ARE RAISED.

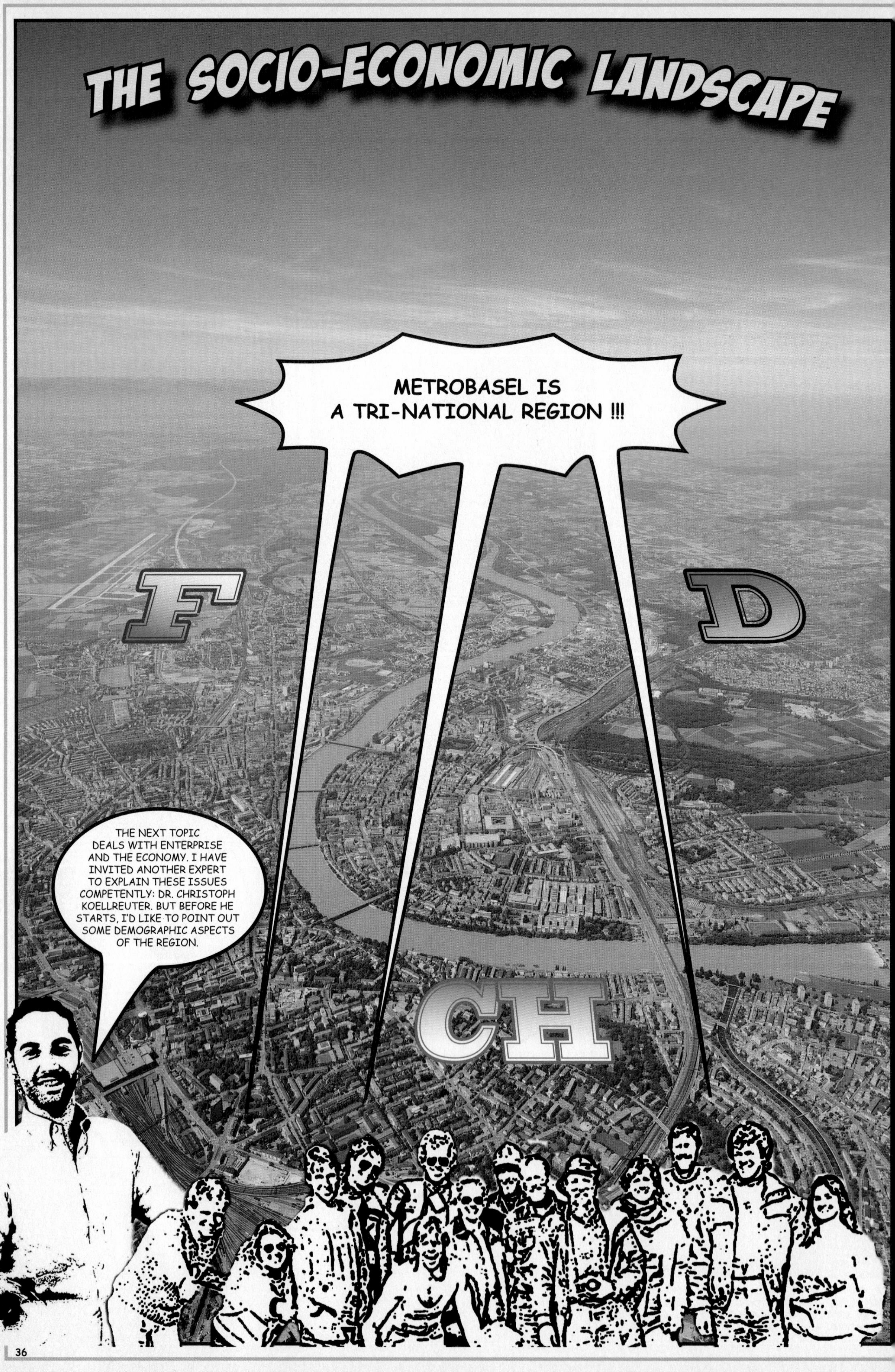
THE SOCIO-ECONOMIC LANDSCAPE
METROBASEL IS A TRI-NATIONAL REGION !!!
F
D
CH
THE NEXT TOPIC DEALS WITH ENTERPRISE AND THE ECONOMY. I HAVE INVITED ANOTHER EXPERT TO EXPLAIN THESE ISSUES COMPETENTLY: DR. CHRISTOPH KOELLREUTER. BUT BEFORE HE STARTS, I'D LIKE TO POINT OUT SOME DEMOGRAPHIC ASPECTS OF THE REGION.

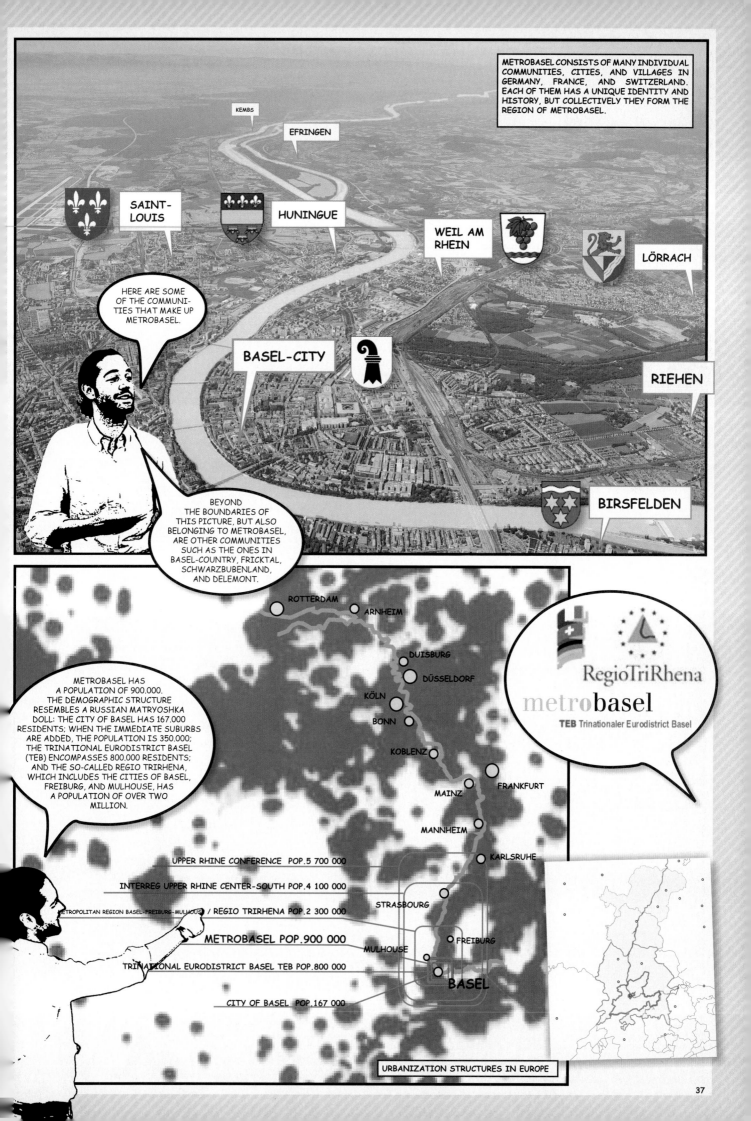

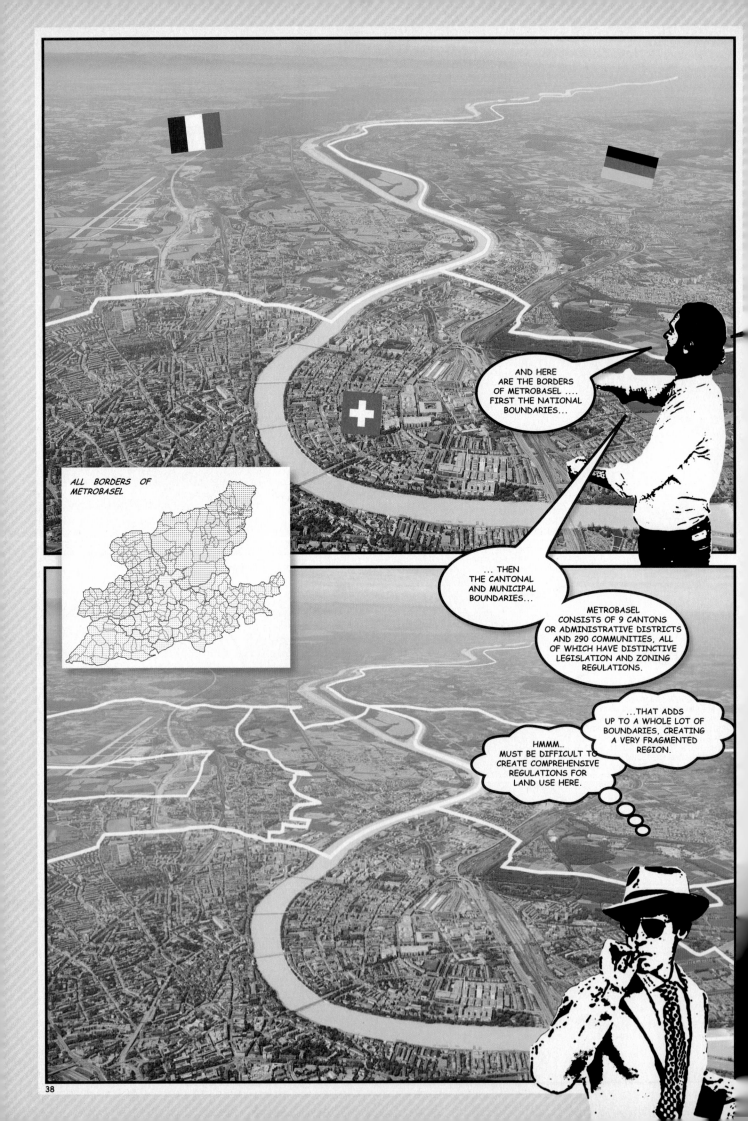

ALL BORDERS OF METROBASEL

AND HERE ARE THE BORDERS OF METROBASEL .... FIRST THE NATIONAL BOUNDARIES...

... THEN THE CANTONAL AND MUNICIPAL BOUNDARIES...

METROBASEL CONSISTS OF 9 CANTONS OR ADMINISTRATIVE DISTRICTS AND 290 COMMUNITIES, ALL OF WHICH HAVE DISTINCTIVE LEGISLATION AND ZONING REGULATIONS.

...THAT ADDS UP TO A WHOLE LOT OF BOUNDARIES, CREATING A VERY FRAGMENTED REGION.

HMMM... MUST BE DIFFICULT TO CREATE COMPREHENSIVE REGULATIONS FOR LAND USE HERE.

CHRISTOPH KOLLREUTER IS THE DIRECTOR OF METROBASEL, AN ASSOCIATION CONCEIVED AS A PLATFORM, VOICE, AND ACTOR FOR THE METROPOLITAN REGION OF BASEL. HE IS FOUNDING MEMBER OF BAK BASEL ECONOMICS, AN ECONOMIC INSTITUTE THAT OPERATES AT THE JUNCTURE OF BUSINESS AND SPATIAL DEVELOPMENT, OUT OF WHICH THE ASSOCIATION METROBASEL DEVELOPED.

INCOME TAX

*IT IS NEAR-IMPOSSIBLE TO DESCRIBE THE NATIONAL TAX RATES IN A FEW MEANIGFUL NUMBERS, SINCE THE TAXATION SYSTEMS CAN ONLY BE COMPARED TO A VERY LIMITED EXTENT DUE TO DIFFERENCES IN AVERAGE WAGES AND TAX BRACKETS. THE FIGURES CITED HERE ARE REFERENCE VALUES.

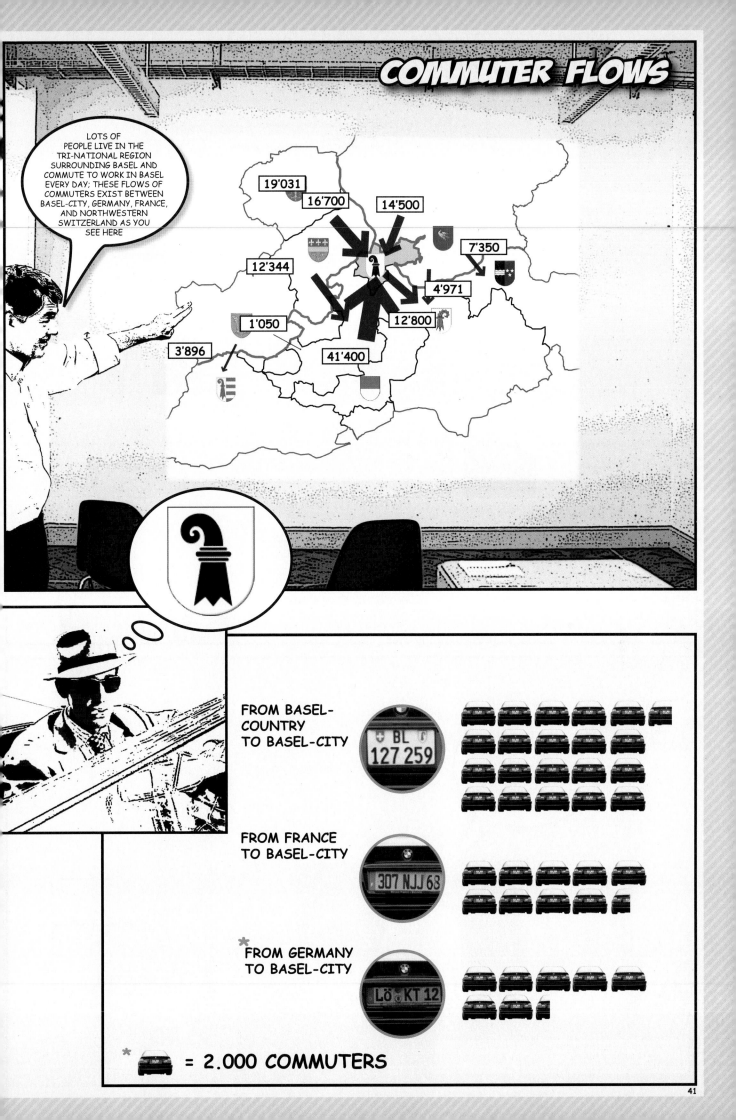

REAL ESTATE PRICES

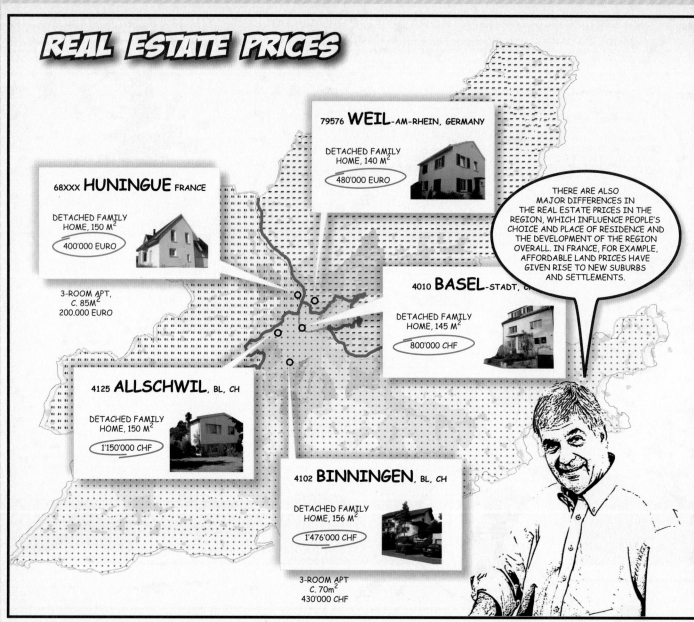

All the above-mentioned data come from the Statistics-Department of Basel-City, as well as from the research done at the ETH Studio Basel.

LIVING IN METRO ∧ BASEL

METROBASEL FEATURES A TYPICAL RANGE OF DIVERSE RESIDENTIAL TYPOLOGIES. IT IS THEREFORE A MODEL EUROPEAN REGION. HOWEVER, IT ALSO HAS STRUCTURAL PROBLEMS, WHICH WE WILL LOOK AT IN DETAIL

SOOHYUN IS AN ARCHITECT FROM THE HARVARD GRADUATE SCHOOL OF DESIGN WHO STUDIED PLANNING METHODOLOGY AT ETH STUDIO BASEL.

47

THE REMODELLING OF THE CITY DURING THE 1970S INTRO- DUCED SOME CONTROVERSIAL NEW STANDARDS.

DOES THAT FIT HERE?

THE VIEW MUST BE GREAT, AND THE APARTMENTS MUST BE QUITE SPACIOUS.

...BUT JUST ONE STREET ALONG, VERY DI- FERENT PROPORTIONS COME INTO VIEW

WHERE HAVE WE ENDED UP NOW??

THIS DOESN'T LOOK VERY URBAN AT ALL... MUCH TOO RURAL.

...ON THE OTHER HAND, EVEN A CITY CENTER SOMETIMES FEA- TURES QUITE LOW HOUSES.

...AND THERE ARE STILL SOME MEDIEVAL BUILDINGS IN THE CENTER TOO.

HEY, LOOK OUT, WE'RE CYCLING DOWN A ONE-WAY STREET THE WRONG WAY!

ON THEIR ARRIVAL AT ETH STUDIO BASEL, THEY ARE GREETED BY SOOHYUN, WHO HAS PREPARED AN OVERVIEW OF RESIDENTIAL BUILDING TYPOLOGIES.

PATRICIA, HOW NICE THAT YOU BROUGHT YOUR FRIEND ALONG. COME UP- STAIRS. THERE'S SOME- THING I WANTED TO SHOW YOU.

CUTE FRIEND...

I'VE PREPARED AN OVERVIEW OF ALL RESIDENTIAL BUILDING TYPOLOGIES IN METROBASEL. THERE ARE QUITE A FEW VARIATIONS AT FIRST GLANCE...

SOOHYUN GUIDES PATRICIA AND MICHEL HROUGH THE VARIOUS BUILDING TYPOLOGIES...D'HABITATIONS...

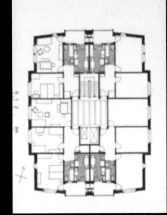

MÜLLHEIMERSTRASSE, 1993

LOOK, THESE ARE TYPICAL APARTMENTS, QUITE SIMILAR TO MY OWN. THERE ARE LOTS OF THESE IN BASEL.

IM SURINAM, 1967

MITTLERESTRASSE, 1951

WIESENPLATZ, 1901

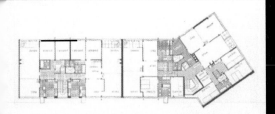

ST ALBAN ANLAGE, 1935

GUNDELDINGERSTRASSE, 1947

HECHTLIACKER, 1965

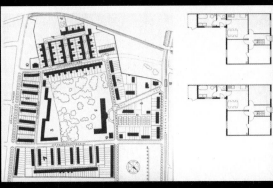

HIRZBRUNNEN, 1934

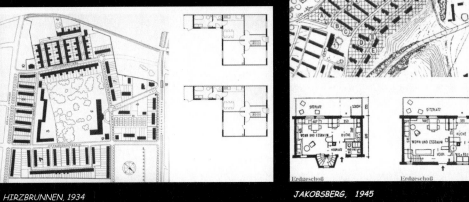

JAKOBSBERG, 1945

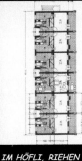

WIESENGARTEN, 1986

IM HÖFLI, RIEHEN

THEY ALL HAVE LOTS OF TINY ROOMS!

...BUT AT SECOND GLANCE, YOU SEE THAT QUITE A FEW APARTMENT TYPES SHARE SIMILAR TRAITS AND FREQUENTLY CONSIST OF MANY SMALL ROOMS. THERE ARE NO OPEN TYPES OF RESIDENCES, LOFTS, OR URBAN DETACHED HOUSES AT ALL IN BASEL. ITS ALSO IMPORTANT TO NOTE THAT BASEL DID NOT EXPERIENCE ANY WARTIME DESTRUCITON, SO THAT MANY OLD RESIDENTIAL BUILDINGS ARE STILL INTACT.

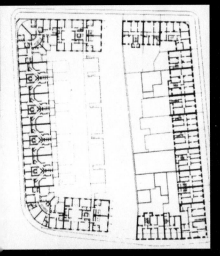

FREIDORF, MUTTENZ, 1924

ROGGENBURGSTRASSE

HOUSING **TYPOLOGY** 1986

WIESENGARTEN , BASEL

HOUSING **TYPOLOGY** 1981

KOMMUNALES WOHNHAUS

HAMMER 1, BASEL

AUTHORS Diener and Diener
DATE 1981
LOCATION Matthäus, Basel, CH
DENSITY 39140inh/km²
SITE AREA 4500m²
FLOOR AREA 2424m²
FAR 3.2
FLOORS 6
TYPE block courtyard

AUTHORS MORGER DEGELO
DATE 1993
LOCATION Matthäus, BS
DENSITY 39140inh/km²
SITE AREA 1737m²
FLOOR AREA 688m²
FAR 2.0
FLOORS 5
TYPE block courtyard

HOUSING **TYPOLOGY** 1935

HISTORIC TYPOLOGY 1944-5

HOUSING **HISTORIC TYPOLOGY** 1933

BATA SIEDLUNG, MÖHLIN

ALBAN, BASEL

SIEDLUNG JAKOBSBERG, BASEL

HOUSING

AUTHORS Hannibal Naef
DATE 1933
LOCATION Möhlin, AG, CH
DENSITY 800inh
SITE AREA 68000m²
FLOOR AREA 1764m²
FAR 0.05
FLOORS 2
TYPE factory town
houses

FLOOR AREA
FAR 3.8
FLOORS 13
TYPE Genossenschafts
tower

*METROBASEL RESIDENTIAL
TYPOLOGIES*

*A SET OF PLAYING CARDS PRODUCED
BY ETH STUDIO BASEL, AVAILABLE IN
ALL MAJOR BOOKSHOPS**

*FORTHCOMING, 2009

IN THE MEETING ROOM, SOOHYUN PRESENTS HER THOUGHTS ON THE TOPIC OF LIVING IN PRIVATE RESIDENCES AND MOVES ON TO THE ASPECT OF DEMOGRAPHICS

IN ADDITION TO RESIDENTIAL TYPOLOGIES, THE QUESTION OF DEMOGRAPHICS IS ALSO QUITE IMPORTANT. HOW MANY PEOPLE LIVE IN THIS REGION? AND HOW IS THE POPULATION DISTRIBUTED?

HERE'S AN INTERESTING FACT: WHILE THE NUMBER OF RESIDENTS HAS BEEN INCREASING, ESPECIALLY SINCE THE 1960S...

WHILE THE REGION IS GROWING...

...THE POPULATION IN THE CITY CENTER IS DECREASING!

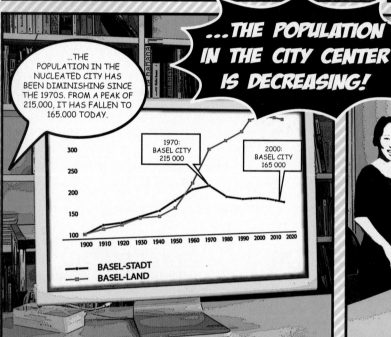

...THE POPULATION IN THE NUCLEATED CITY HAS BEEN DIMINISHING SINCE THE 1970S. FROM A PEAK OF 215.000, IT HAS FALLEN TO 165.000 TODAY.

IF THE POPULATION OF THE ENTIRE TRI-NATIONAL REGION CONTINUES TO GROW, BUT THE POPULATION OF THE CITY CENTER SHRINKS...

...WE HAVE TO ANALYZE THE PROPORTION BETWEEN THE NUCLEUS AND THE ENVIRONS AND TRY TO UNDERSTAND WHY PEOPLE ARE LEAVING THE CITY CENTER.

ONE IMPORTANT REASON IS THE LACK OF LIVING SPACE AND THE LIMITED RANGE OF HOUSING SUPPLY IN BASEL-CITY.

BASEL-CITY NEEDS MORE LIVING SPACE!

WHAT DENSITY CAN BASEL SUSTAIN?

LOOKING AT THE CITY CENTER, IT APPEARS TO BE COMPLETELY BUILT UP AND TO FEATURE A HIGH DENSITY...

...DESPITE THE DECLINING POPULATION IN THE CENTER, THERE HAS BEEN LOTS OF CONSTRUCTION IN BASEL-CITY...

...BECAUSE THE AVERAGE APARTMENT SIZE IS INCREASING* AND A LOT OF CONSTRUCTION CONSISTS OF OFFICE AND COMMERCIAL SPACE. THE QUESTION IS: WHAT DENSITY IS SUSTAINABLE FOR BASEL?

DEVELOPMENT PROJECT ERLEN-MATT

*BETWEEN 1970 AND 2005, THE LIVING SPACE PER PERSON NEARLY DOUBLED FROM 23SQM TO 45SQM.

BASEL HAS ABOUT 7.200 RESIDENTS PER SQUARE KILOMETER. LET'S COMPARE THAT TO OTHER CITIES.

COMPARISON OF DENSITY WITH OTHER CITIES

THERE ARE A NUMBER OF CITIES THAT ARE MUCH MORE DENSE AND OF COURSE SOME THAT HAVE A LOWER DENSITY THAN BASEL... IN THE NUCLEATED CITY, THERE ARE 7.200 RESIDENTS PER SQUARE KILOMETER. ACROSS THE ENTIRE METROBASEL REGION, THERE ARE 435 PEOPLE PER SQUARE KILOMETER. LET'S COMPARE.

BARCELONA HAS A POPULATION DENSITY OF 16.000 RESIDENTS/KM². IN THE CITY CENTER, BUILDINGS ARE USUALLY SIX FLOORS HIGH.

HOUSTON HAS 1.400 RESIDENTS PER KM², MAINLY IN THE SUBURBS WITH ONE- OR TWO-FLOOR HOUSING

AT 26.000 RESIDENTS PER KM², MANHATTAN IS ONE OF THE WORLD'S MOST DENSELY POPULATED CITIES.

SO BASEL'S POPULATION DENSITY ISN'T REALLY ALL THAT HIGH COMPARED TO OTHER CITIES. THAT MAY EXPLAIN WHY BASEL RESEMBLED A SMALL TOWN IN SOME PLACES DURING THE BICYCLE TOUR.

BERLIN HAS 10.000 RESIDENTS PER KM². IN THE CITY CENTER, AN AVERAGE BUILDING IS SEVEN FLOORS HIGH.

SO WE SEE THAT DENSITY IN A CITY CAN BE DEALT WITH IN VERY DIFFERENT WAYS. WE COULD UTILIZE SOME OF THESE IDEAS FOR ADDITIONAL RESIDENTIAL CONSTRUCTION.

THERE ARE VARIOUS PLANNING INSTRUMENTS FOR REGULATING POPULATION DENSITY IN A CITY. ONE OF THE MOST IMPORTANT IS THE ZONING PLAN... BÂLE-VILLE.

LET'S GET **FRITZ SCHUMACHER**, THE CANTONAL ARCHITECT OF BASEL-STADT, TO EXPLAIN WHAT IT IS AND HOW IT WORKS.

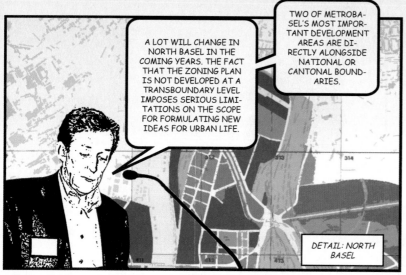

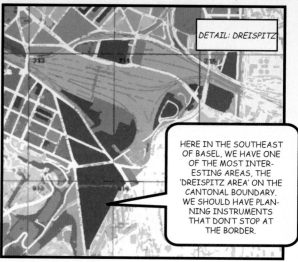

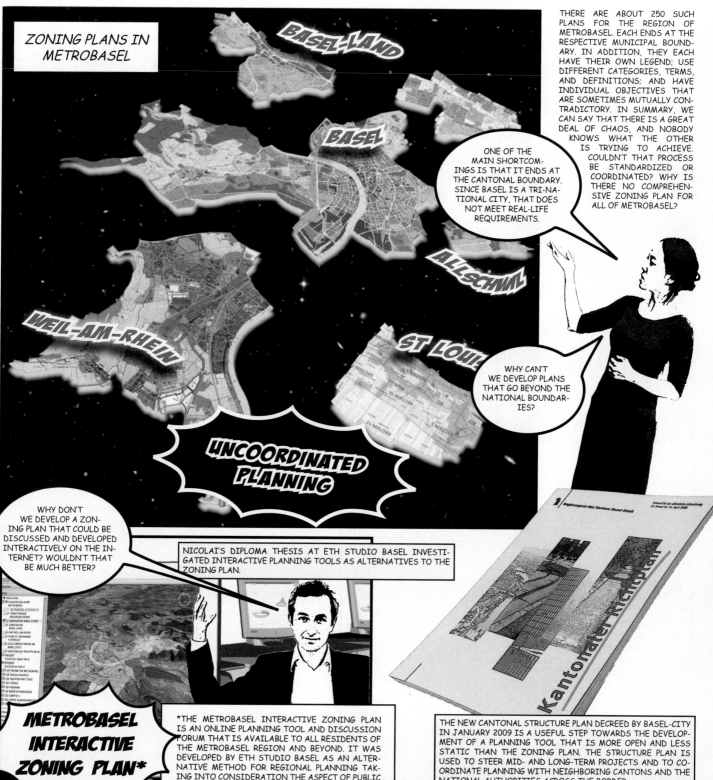

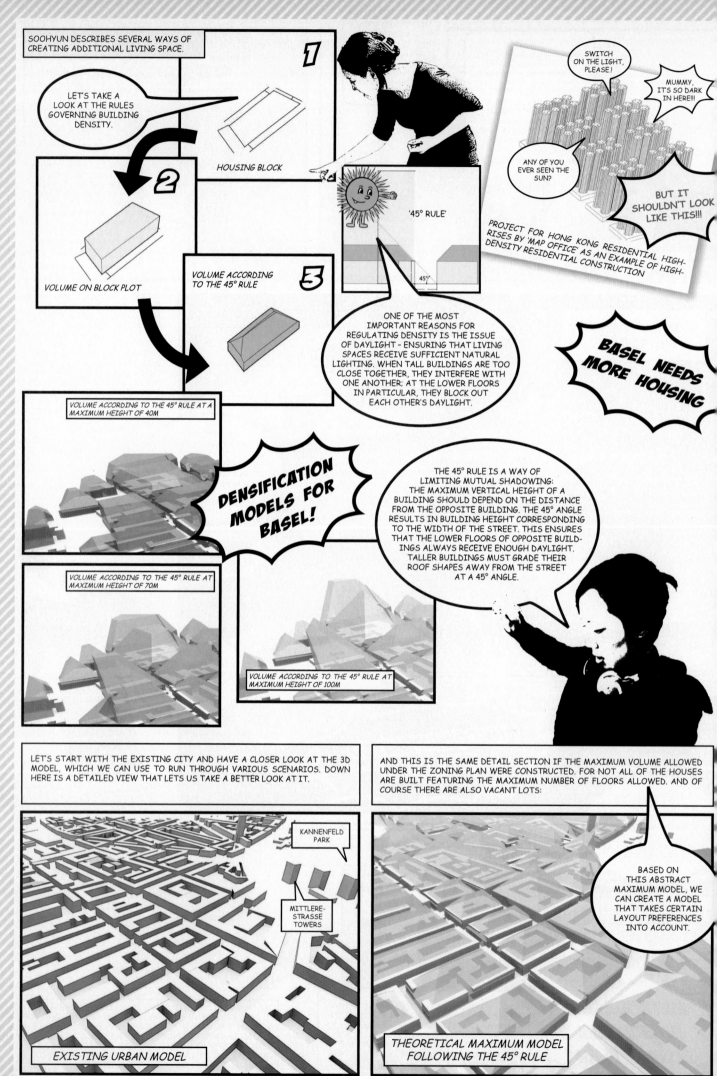

SOOHYUN DESCRIBES SEVERAL WAYS OF CREATING ADDITIONAL LIVING SPACE.

LET'S TAKE A LOOK AT THE RULES GOVERNING BUILDING DENSITY.

1

HOUSING BLOCK

2

VOLUME ON BLOCK PLOT

3

VOLUME ACCORDING TO THE 45° RULE

'45° RULE'

45°

SWITCH ON THE LIGHT, PLEASE!

MUMMY, IT'S SO DARK IN HERE!!!

ANY OF YOU EVER SEEN THE SUN?

BUT IT SHOULDN'T LOOK LIKE THIS!!!

PROJECT FOR HONG KONG RESIDENTIAL HIGH-RISES BY 'MAP OFFICE' AS AN EXAMPLE OF HIGH-DENSITY RESIDENTIAL CONSTRUCTION

ONE OF THE MOST IMPORTANT REASONS FOR REGULATING DENSITY IS THE ISSUE OF DAYLIGHT - ENSURING THAT LIVING SPACES RECEIVE SUFFICIENT NATURAL LIGHTING. WHEN TALL BUILDINGS ARE TOO CLOSE TOGETHER, THEY INTERFERE WITH ONE ANOTHER; AT THE LOWER FLOORS IN PARTICULAR, THEY BLOCK OUT EACH OTHER'S DAYLIGHT.

BASEL NEEDS MORE HOUSING

VOLUME ACCORDING TO THE 45° RULE AT A MAXIMUM HEIGHT OF 40M

DENSIFICATION MODELS FOR BASEL!

THE 45° RULE IS A WAY OF LIMITING MUTUAL SHADOWING: THE MAXIMUM VERTICAL HEIGHT OF A BUILDING SHOULD DEPEND ON THE DISTANCE FROM THE OPPOSITE BUILDING. THE 45° ANGLE RESULTS IN BUILDING HEIGHT CORRESPONDING TO THE WIDTH OF THE STREET. THIS ENSURES THAT THE LOWER FLOORS OF OPPOSITE BUILD-INGS ALWAYS RECEIVE ENOUGH DAYLIGHT. TALLER BUILDINGS MUST GRADE THEIR ROOF SHAPES AWAY FROM THE STREET AT A 45° ANGLE.

VOLUME ACCORDING TO THE 45° RULE AT MAXIMUM HEIGHT OF 70M

VOLUME ACCORDING TO THE 45° RULE AT MAXIMUM HEIGHT OF 100M

LET'S START WITH THE EXISTING CITY AND HAVE A CLOSER LOOK AT THE 3D MODEL, WHICH WE CAN USE TO RUN THROUGH VARIOUS SCENARIOS. DOWN HERE IS A DETAILED VIEW THAT LETS US TAKE A BETTER LOOK AT IT.

AND THIS IS THE SAME DETAIL SECTION IF THE MAXIMUM VOLUME ALLOWED UNDER THE ZONING PLAN WERE CONSTRUCTED. FOR NOT ALL OF THE HOUSES ARE BUILT FEATURING THE MAXIMUM NUMBER OF FLOORS ALLOWED. AND OF COURSE THERE ARE ALSO VACANT LOTS:

KANNENFELD PARK

MITTLERE-STRASSE TOWERS

BASED ON THIS ABSTRACT MAXIMUM MODEL, WE CAN CREATE A MODEL THAT TAKES CERTAIN LAYOUT PREFERENCES INTO ACCOUNT.

EXISTING URBAN MODEL

THEORETICAL MAXIMUM MODEL FOLLOWING THE 45° RULE

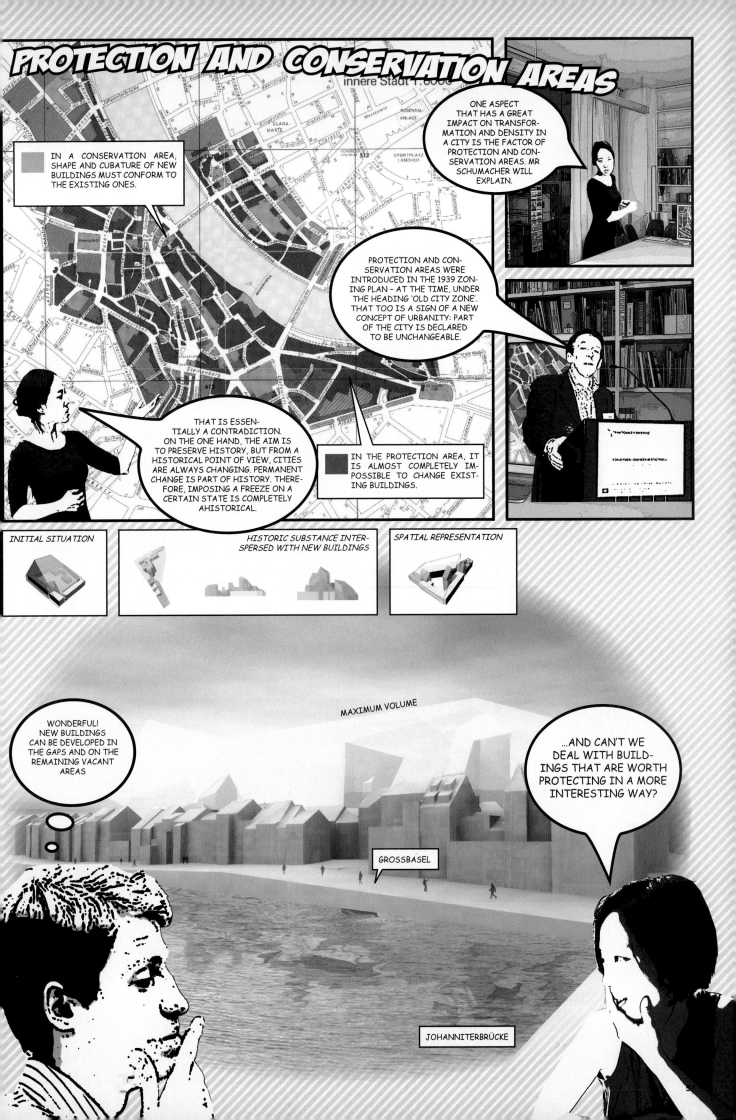

AFTER THIS OVERVIEW OF RESIDENTIAL TYPOLOGIES, PATRICIA AND MICHEL START OFF AGAIN FOR A CYCLING TOUR ALONG THE RHINE.

LOOK, IT MUST BE GREAT TO LIVE HERE.

HMMM. GREAT VIEW!

...BUT AFTER A FEW RESIDENTIAL BUILDINGS, THE PATH ALONG THE RHINE IS ALREADY BARRED...

THAT'S THE END OF THE PATH. IT'S PROBABLY BEST TO CROSS THE RHINE.

IT'S STRANGE THAT YOU CAN'T CYCLE ALONG THE RHINE.

WHILE PATRICIA AND MICHEL TAKE A DETOUR IN ORDER TO GET BACK TO THE RIVER BANK, THEY NOTICE A HIGH-RISE APARTMENT BLOCK WHOSE VIEW OF THE RIVER IS UNFORTUNATELY BLOCKED...

LIVING ON THE RHINE

OH MAN, WHY CAN'T I SEE THE RIVER??

YEAH, RIGHT! WHY NOT LIVE DOWN BY THE RIVER? THAT'S THE NICEST PART OF TOWN, AFTER ALL!

THIS IS ‚MITTLERE BRÜCKE'. I'LL TELL YOU MORE ABOUT IT LATER.*

THEY CROSS MITTLERE BRÜCKE...

IN THE CHAPTER 'MOVING'*

...AND REACH THE OTHER SIDE OF THE RIVER...

BEAUTIFUL! THIS IS ALMOST IDYLLIC.

WE OUGHT TO HAVE AN IDEAL VIEW FROM OVER THERE...

PATRICIA HAD A PLACE IN MIND THAT MUST BE A FANTASTIC PLACE TO LIVE...

SHE ALREADY HAD SOME PRETTY CLEAR IDEAS AS TO WHAT IT WOULD BE LIKE TO LIVE IN SUCH A PLACE. MAYBE AS IF ONE WERE SUSPENDED ABOVE THE ENTIRE CITY...* AND IN A VERY UNUSUAL KIND OF APARTMENT.

*MODELED ON THE HOUSE OF PIERRE KOENIG, CAPTURED IN A FAMOUS PHOTO BY JULIUS SHULMAN.

WHITE HOUSE AND BLUE HOUSE – TODAY, THE DEPARTMENT OF JUSTICE

THERE ARE ONLY VERY FEW HOMES HERE. MOST ARE OFFICES AND ADMINISTRATIVE BUILDINGS.

OH, IT WOULD BE WONDERFUL TO LIVE IN THIS BLUE HOUSE. WHAT A LOVELY VIEW ACROSS THE CITY.

ALLOTMENT GARDENS ON THE RHINE

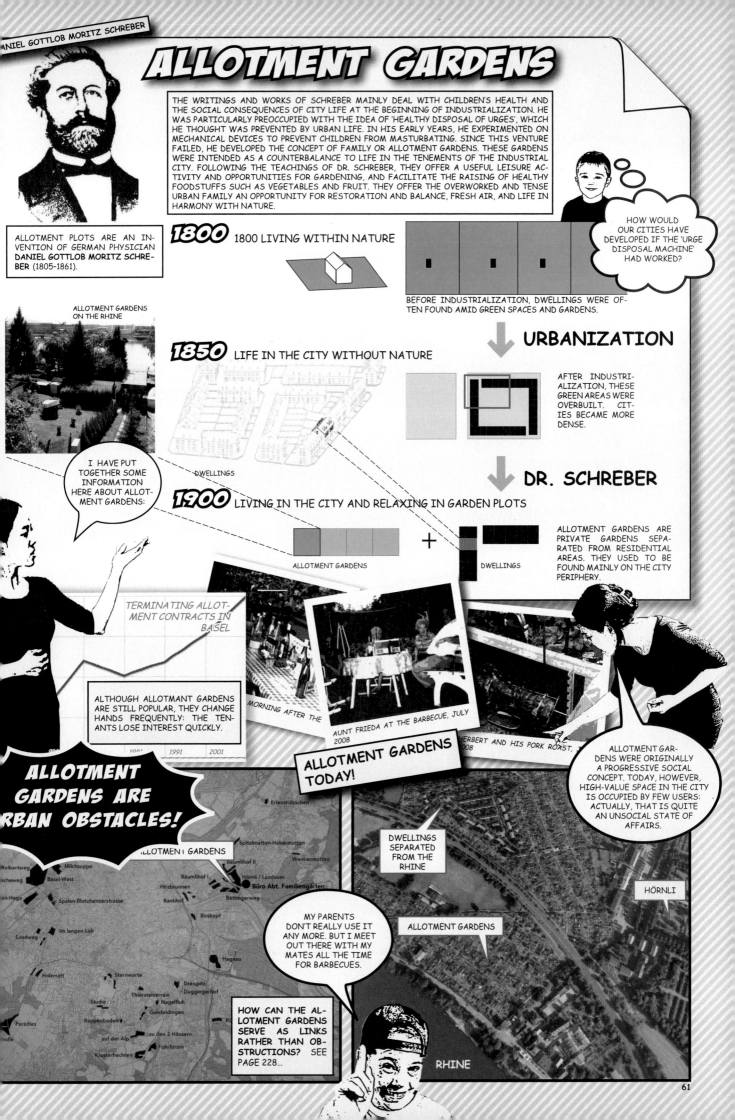

ALLOTMENT GARDENS

DANIEL GOTTLOB MORITZ SCHREBER

THE WRITINGS AND WORKS OF SCHREBER MAINLY DEAL WITH CHILDREN'S HEALTH AND THE SOCIAL CONSEQUENCES OF CITY LIFE AT THE BEGINNING OF INDUSTRIALIZATION. HE WAS PARTICULARLY PREOCCUPIED WITH THE IDEA OF 'HEALTHY DISPOSAL OF URGES', WHICH HE THOUGHT WAS PREVENTED BY URBAN LIFE. IN HIS EARLY YEARS, HE EXPERIMENTED ON MECHANICAL DEVICES TO PREVENT CHILDREN FROM MASTURBATING. SINCE THIS VENTURE FAILED, HE DEVELOPED THE CONCEPT OF FAMILY OR ALLOTMENT GARDENS. THESE GARDENS WERE INTENDED AS A COUNTERBALANCE TO LIFE IN THE TENEMENTS OF THE INDUSTRIAL CITY. FOLLOWING THE TEACHINGS OF DR. SCHREBER, THEY OFFER A USEFUL LEISURE ACTIVITY AND OPPORTUNITIES FOR GARDENING, AND FACILITATE THE RAISING OF HEALTHY FOODSTUFFS SUCH AS VEGETABLES AND FRUIT. THEY OFFER THE OVERWORKED AND TENSE URBAN FAMILY AN OPPORTUNITY FOR RESTORATION AND BALANCE, FRESH AIR, AND LIFE IN HARMONY WITH NATURE.

HOW WOULD OUR CITIES HAVE DEVELOPED IF THE 'URGE DISPOSAL MACHINE' HAD WORKED?

ALLOTMENT PLOTS ARE AN INVENTION OF GERMAN PHYSICIAN DANIEL GOTTLOB MORITZ SCHREBER (1805-1861).

1800 1800 LIVING WITHIN NATURE

BEFORE INDUSTRIALIZATION, DWELLINGS WERE OFTEN FOUND AMID GREEN SPACES AND GARDENS.

ALLOTMENT GARDENS ON THE RHINE

URBANIZATION

1850 LIFE IN THE CITY WITHOUT NATURE

AFTER INDUSTRIALIZATION, THESE GREEN AREAS WERE OVERBUILT. CITIES BECAME MORE DENSE.

DWELLINGS

I HAVE PUT TOGETHER SOME INFORMATION HERE ABOUT ALLOTMENT GARDENS:

DR. SCHREBER

1900 LIVING IN THE CITY AND RELAXING IN GARDEN PLOTS

ALLOTMENT GARDENS ARE PRIVATE GARDENS SEPARATED FROM RESIDENTIAL AREAS. THEY USED TO BE FOUND MAINLY ON THE CITY PERIPHERY.

ALLOTMENT GARDENS + DWELLINGS

TERMINATING ALLOTMENT CONTRACTS IN BASEL

ALTHOUGH ALLOTMANT GARDENS ARE STILL POPULAR, THEY CHANGE HANDS FREQUENTLY: THE TENANTS LOSE INTEREST QUICKLY.

1991   2001

MORNING AFTER THE

AUNT FRIEDA AT THE BARBECUE, JULY 2008

HERBERT AND HIS PORK ROAST, 2008

ALLOTMENT GARDENS ARE RBAN OBSTACLES!

ALLOTMENT GARDENS TODAY!

ALLOTMENT GARDENS WERE ORIGINALLY A PROGRESSIVE SOCIAL CONCEPT. TODAY, HOWEVER, HIGH-VALUE SPACE IN THE CITY IS OCCUPIED BY FEW USERS: ACTUALLY, THAT IS QUITE AN UNSOCIAL STATE OF AFFAIRS.

Erlenstrasschen
Spitalmatten-Habermatten
ALLOTMEN T GARDENS
Reibertweg   Milchsuppe
Baumlihof II   Wenkenmatten
scheweg   Basel-West
Baumlihof I   Hörnli / Landauer
an-Hega   Spalen-Blotzheimerstrasse
Hirzbrunnen   Büro Abt. Familiengärten
Rankhof   Bettingerweg
Sandweg   im langen Loh
Birskopf
Holzmatt   Sternwarte
Hagnau
Studio   Thiersteinerrain
Dreispitz
Nagelfluh   Duggingerhof
Paradies   Rappenboden   Gundeldingen
auf der Alp   zu den 3 Häusern
Fohrlisrain
Klosterfiechten

DWELLINGS SEPARATED FROM THE RHINE

HÖRNLI

ALLOTMENT GARDENS

MY PARENTS DON'T REALLY USE IT ANY MORE. BUT I MEET OUT THERE WITH MY MATES ALL THE TIME FOR BARBECUES.

HOW CAN THE ALLOTMENT GARDENS SERVE AS LINKS RATHER THAN OBSTRUCTIONS? SEE PAGE 228...

RHINE

Der neue
Basler Zentralfriedhof

AND THEN THERE'S THE HÖRNLI CEMETERY.

IT ALSO OCCUPIES SOME OF THE PRIME REAL ESTATE IN THE CITY CENTER: AT THE FOOT OF A HILL, WITH A VIEW OF THE ENTIRE REGION.

THE CENTRAL CEMETERY AT THE HÖRNLI CONFORMED TO THE IDEAL TYPE OF A CEMETERY WHEN IT WAS ESTABLISHED IN 1932. DUE TO THE RAPID POPULATION GROWTH IN THE 19TH CENTURY, THE MANY SMALLER GRAVEYARDS THAT HAD PREVIOUSLY BEEN USED REACHED THE LIMITS OF THEIR CAPACITY. IN PREVIOUS TIMES, SMALLER BURIAL GROUNDS JUST OUTSIDE THE CITY WALLS HAD BEEN USED. THE CENTRAL CEMETERY WAS BASED ON THE IDEA OF CLOSING ALL THE GRAVES IN THE SMALLER GRAVEYARDS AND TRANSFERRING THEM TO A CENTRAL PLACE. IT WAS PROBABLY THE BIGGEST 'RELOCATION' PROJECT IN THE HISTORY OF THE CITY. THE IDEA IS SOUND; UNFORTUNATELY, THE LOCATION SELECTED FOR IT IS ONE THAT WOULD BE IDEAL FOR LIVING QUARTERS.

KLEINHÜNINGEN CEMETERY

HORBURG CEMETERY

HÖRNLI

KANNENFELD CEMETERY

SPALEN CEMETERY

WOLF CEMETERY

RELOCATION OF CEMETERIES TO THE CENTRAL CEMETERY AT HÖRNLI

HMMM. THE IDEA OF DISTRIBUTED GRAVEYARDS ISN'T SO BAD AFTERALL. THEN WE COULD BUILD A NEW RESIDENTIAL QUARTER IN EXCELLENT LOCATION WHERE THE CENTRAL CEMETERY IS NOW.

LIVING ON THE RHINE

BASEL ... COULD IT REALLY BE LIKE 'LA SERENISSIMA'?*

*'LA SERENISSIMA' IS A NAME FOR VENICE, REFERRING TO ITS BEAUTY AND 'GREAT SERENITY'.

BACK AT ETH STUDIO BASEL, SOOHYUN PRESENTS SOME OF HER THOUGHTS ON THIS TOPIC:

LET'S TAKE THOSE NICE HOUSES ON OBERER RHEINWEG, FOR EXAMPLE...

OBERER RHEINWEG, KLEINBASEL

OBERER RHEINWEG, KLEINBASEL

... AND COMBINE THAT WITH A SLIGHTLY HIGHER DENSITY...

ON THE EAST RIVER IN NEW YORK

SCHAFFHAUSERRHEINWEG, KLEINBASEL

ON THE RHINE AT BASEL, VIEW FROM BIRSFELDEN HYDROELECTRIC PLANT

CAN'T WE DEVELOP TYPES OF RESIDENCE THAT MAKE MUCH BETTER USE OF THE QUALITIES OF URBAN LIFESTYLE?

...WE COULD CREATE AN 'UPPER EAST SIDE' AT THE HÖRNLI

WOW! HOW EXCITING! THAT WOULD BE ALMOST LIKE NEW YORK...

64

"BORNEO-SPORENBURG À AMSTERDAM

LIVING ON THE RHINE

BORNEO SPORENBURG IN AMSTERDAM IS A GREAT EXAMPLE OF HOW TO CONSTRUCT DENSE DETACHED HOUSING BY THE WATER

EXAMPLE: BORNEO SPORENBURG IN AMSTERDAM

LIVING ON THE RHINE BY THE HÖRNLI

MODEL CONCEPT

LIVING ON THE WATERFRONT

HIRZBRUNNEN

HÖRNLI

THERE IS ENOUGH SPACE HERE FOR 1.900 PATIO HOUSES, 640 APARTMENTS, AND 120.000 SQUARE METERS OF OFFICE AND COMMERCIAL SPACE.

THE RHINE

BIRSFELDEN

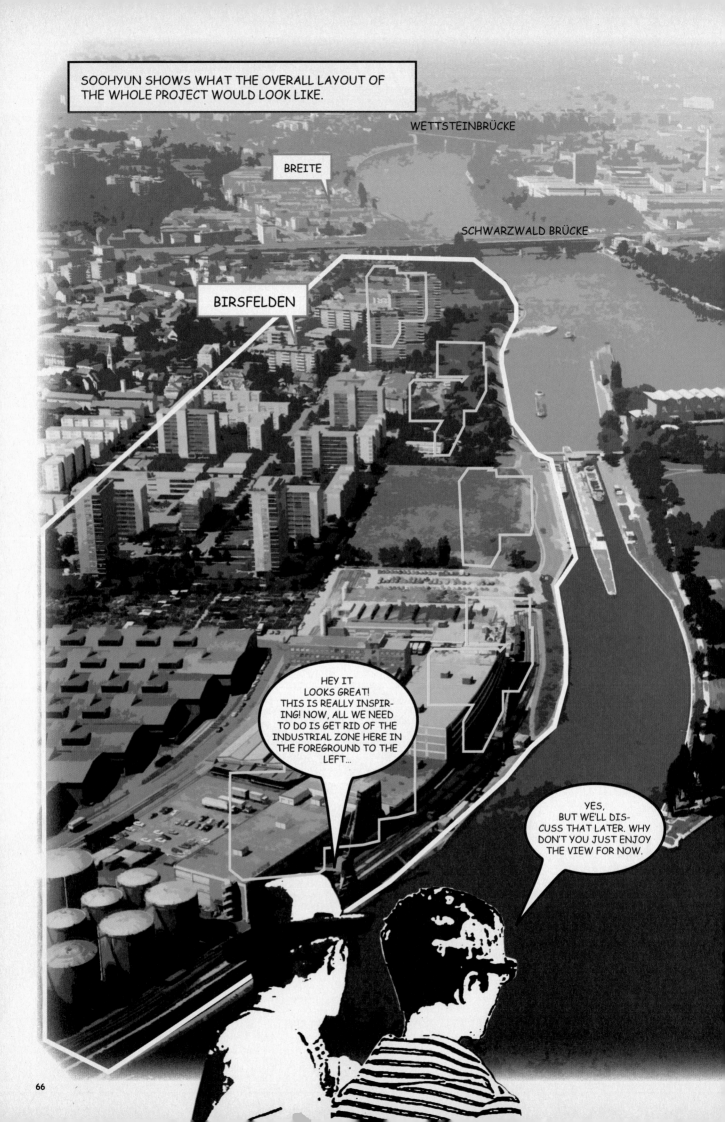

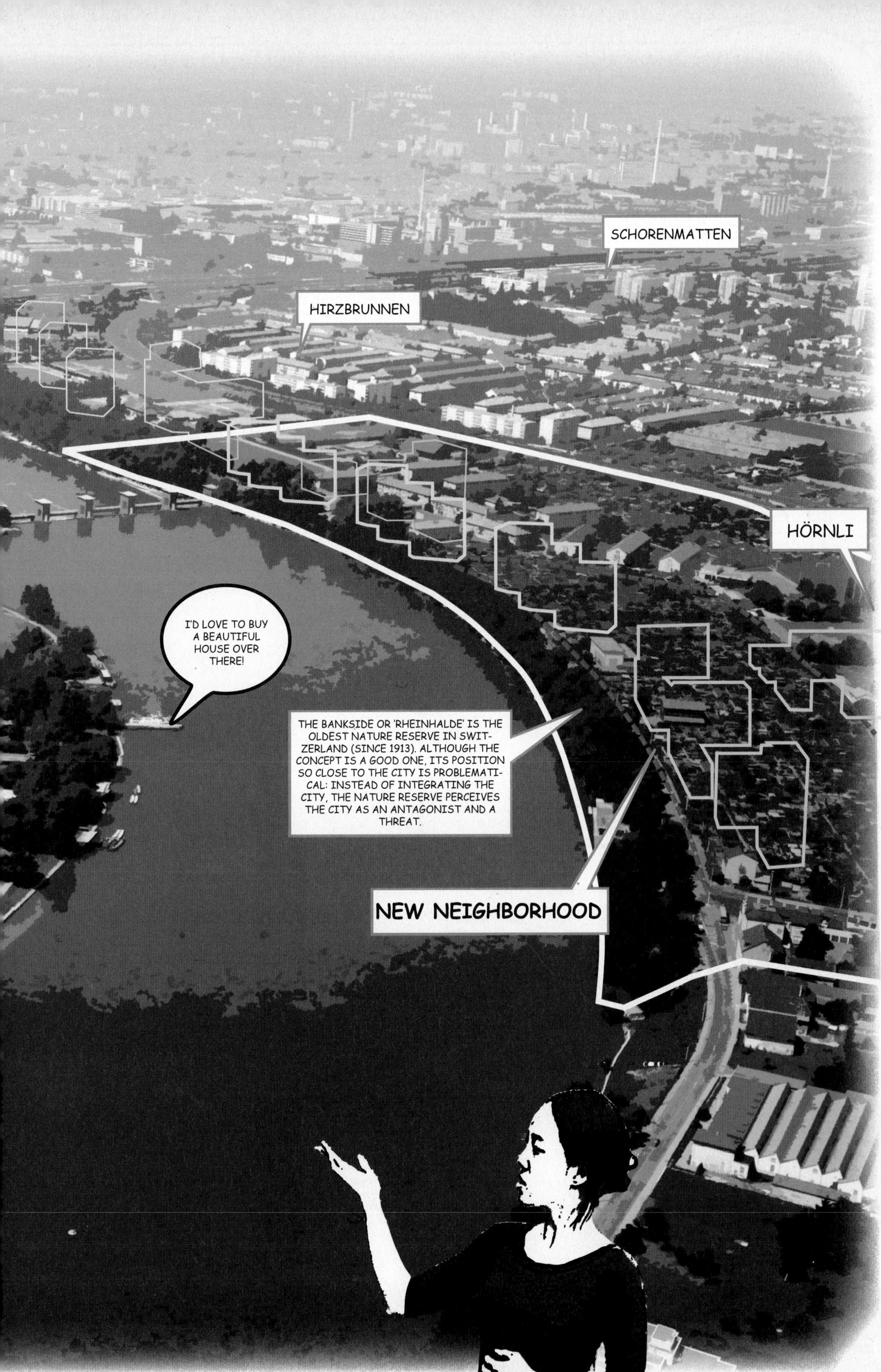
SCHORENMATTEN
HIRZBRUNNEN
HÖRNLI
I'D LOVE TO BUY A BEAUTIFUL HOUSE OVER THERE!
THE BANKSIDE OR 'RHEINHALDE' IS THE OLDEST NATURE RESERVE IN SWITZERLAND (SINCE 1913). ALTHOUGH THE CONCEPT IS A GOOD ONE, ITS POSITION SO CLOSE TO THE CITY IS PROBLEMATICAL: INSTEAD OF INTEGRATING THE CITY, THE NATURE RESERVE PERCEIVES THE CITY AS AN ANTAGONIST AND A THREAT.
NEW NEIGHBORHOOD

THE MODEL:

SURROUNDING CONSTRUCTION
(COULD BE HIGHER AND MORE DENSE)

KANNENFELD PARK

THE MODEL OF A PARK SURROUNDED BY BUILDINGS IS ONE OPTION FOR COMPACTING THE CITY THAT STARTS OFF WITH GREEN ZONES AND AIMS TO CREATE ATTRACTIVE PLACES FOR LIVING AND RECREATION.

PARK SURROUNDED BY BUILDINGS

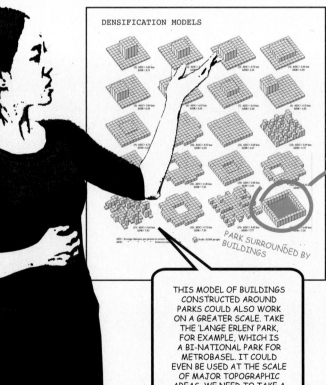

DENSIFICATION MODELS

PARK SURROUNDED BY BUILDINGS

THIS MODEL OF BUILDINGS CONSTRUCTED AROUND PARKS COULD ALSO WORK ON A GREATER SCALE. TAKE THE 'LANGE ERLEN' PARK, FOR EXAMPLE, WHICH IS A BI-NATIONAL PARK FOR METROBASEL. IT COULD EVEN BE USED AT THE SCALE OF MAJOR TOPOGRAPHIC AREAS. WE NEED TO TAKE A CLOSER LOOK AT THIS...

CENTRAL PARK, NEW YORK | 3.2 KM²
9.7 KM

LANGEN ERLEN, WEIL-AM-RHEIN (D) | 5.7 KM²
11.8 KM

DENSIFIED EDGE

DENSIFIED EDGE

LANGEN ERLEN, BASEL

METROBASEL 'CENTRAL PARK'

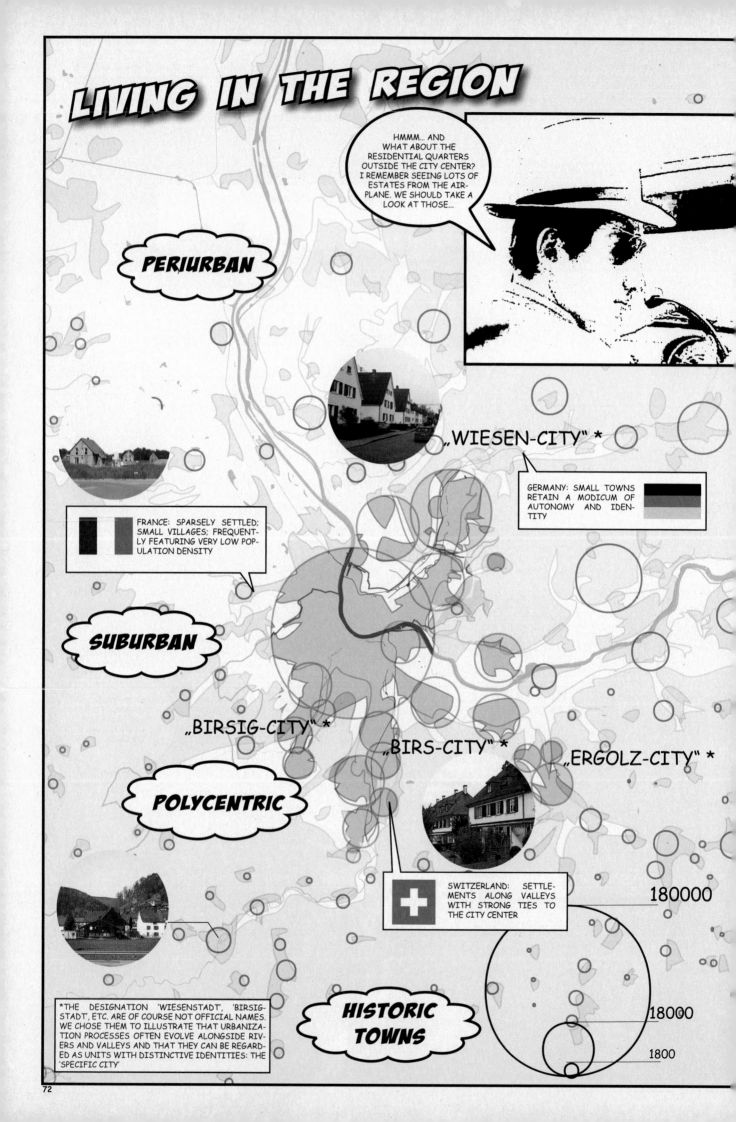

LIVING IN THE REGION

HMMM... AND WHAT ABOUT THE RESIDENTIAL QUARTERS OUTSIDE THE CITY CENTER? I REMEMBER SEEING LOTS OF ESTATES FROM THE AIRPLANE. WE SHOULD TAKE A LOOK AT THOSE...

PERIURBAN

„WIESEN-CITY" *

GERMANY: SMALL TOWNS RETAIN A MODICUM OF AUTONOMY AND IDENTITY

FRANCE: SPARSELY SETTLED; SMALL VILLAGES; FREQUENTLY FEATURING VERY LOW POPULATION DENSITY

SUBURBAN

„BIRSIG-CITY" *

„BIRS-CITY" *

„ERGOLZ-CITY" *

POLYCENTRIC

SWITZERLAND: SETTLEMENTS ALONG VALLEYS WITH STRONG TIES TO THE CITY CENTER

180000

18000

1800

*THE DESIGNATION 'WIESENSTADT', 'BIRSIGSTADT', ETC. ARE OF COURSE NOT OFFICIAL NAMES. WE CHOSE THEM TO ILLUSTRATE THAT URBANIZATION PROCESSES OFTEN EVOLVE ALONGSIDE RIVERS AND VALLEYS AND THAT THEY CAN BE REGARDED AS UNITS WITH DISTINCTIVE IDENTITIES: THE 'SPECIFIC CITY'

HISTORIC TOWNS

ERGOLZ-CITY: MUTTENZ FREIDORF

WIESEN-CITY: WEIL-AM-RHEIN

SUBURBAN

HISTORIC TOWNS

BIRS-CITY : DORNACH

BIRSIG-CITY: BINNINGEN

PERIURBAN

BIRSIG-CITY : LAUFEN

BIRSIG-CITY: DELEMONT

AS WE CAN SEE, METROBASEL CONSISTS OF MULTIPLE EPICEN-TERS WITH THEIR OWN POPULA-TIONS

THE SUNDGAU IS A PARTICULARLY FAST-GROWING REGION OF METROBASEL!

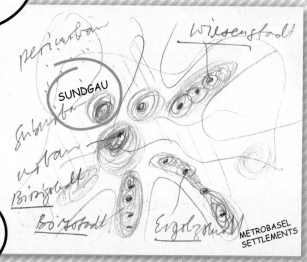

METROBASEL SETTLEMENTS

73

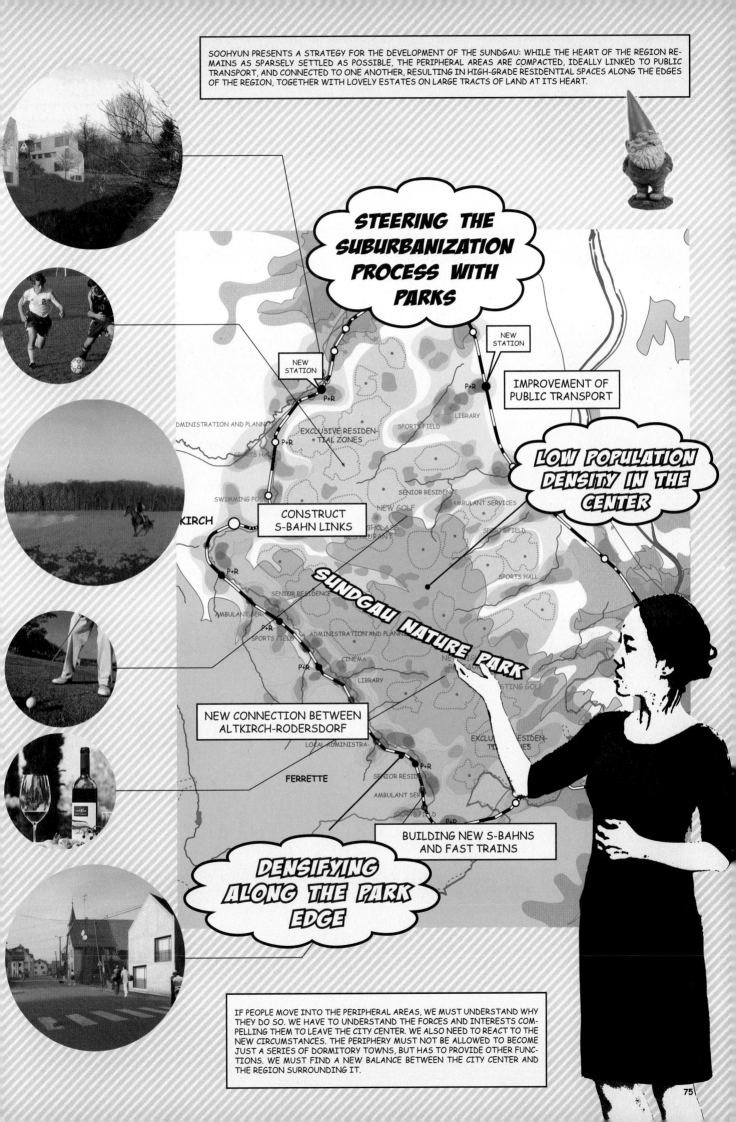

SOOHYUN PRESENTS A STRATEGY FOR THE DEVELOPMENT OF THE SUNDGAU: WHILE THE HEART OF THE REGION RE-MAINS AS SPARSELY SETTLED AS POSSIBLE, THE PERIPHERAL AREAS ARE COMPACTED, IDEALLY LINKED TO PUBLIC TRANSPORT, AND CONNECTED TO ONE ANOTHER, RESULTING IN HIGH-GRADE RESIDENTIAL SPACES ALONG THE EDGES OF THE REGION, TOGETHER WITH LOVELY ESTATES ON LARGE TRACTS OF LAND AT ITS HEART.

STEERING THE SUBURBANIZATION PROCESS WITH PARKS

NEW STATION

NEW STATION

IMPROVEMENT OF PUBLIC TRANSPORT

LOW POPULATION DENSITY IN THE CENTER

EXCLUSIVE RESIDEN-TIAL ZONES

ADMINISTRATION AND PLANNING

SPORTS FIELD

LIBRARY

SPORTS HALL

SWIMMING POOL

SENIOR RESIDENCE

AMBULANT SERVICES

CONSTRUCT S-BAHN LINKS

KIRCH

NEW GOLF

HIGHCLASS RESTAURANT

SPORTS FIELD

SPORTS HALL

SENIOR RESIDENCE

AMBULANT SER

SPORTS FIELD

ADMINISTRATION AND PLANNING

SUNDGAU NATURE PARK

CINEMA

LIBRARY

NEW HIGH-CLASS RESTAURANT

TESTING GOLF

EXCLU RESIDEN-TI ES

NEW CONNECTION BETWEEN ALTKIRCH-RODERSDORF

LOCAL ADMINISTRA-

FERRETTE

SENIOR RESIDENCE

AMBULANT SER

SPORTS FIELD

DENSIFYING ALONG THE PARK EDGE

BUILDING NEW S-BAHNS AND FAST TRAINS

IF PEOPLE MOVE INTO THE PERIPHERAL AREAS, WE MUST UNDERSTAND WHY THEY DO SO. WE HAVE TO UNDERSTAND THE FORCES AND INTERESTS COM-PELLING THEM TO LEAVE THE CITY CENTER. WE ALSO NEED TO REACT TO THE NEW CIRCUMSTANCES. THE PERIPHERY MUST NOT BE ALLOWED TO BECOME JUST A SERIES OF DORMITORY TOWNS, BUT HAS TO PROVIDE OTHER FUNC-TIONS. WE MUST FIND A NEW BALANCE BETWEEN THE CITY CENTER AND THE REGION SURROUNDING IT.

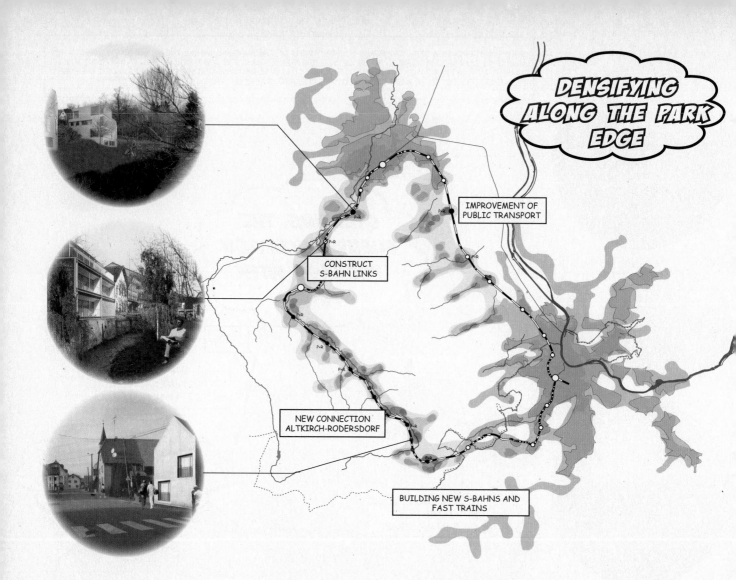

DENSIFYING ALONG THE PARK EDGE

IMPROVEMENT OF PUBLIC TRANSPORT

CONSTRUCT S-BAHN LINKS

NEW CONNECTION ALTKIRCH-RODERSDORF

BUILDING NEW S-BAHNS AND FAST TRAINS

LIVING ON THE RIVER ILL

DENSIFIED VILLAGES

SUNDGAU

PETIT CAMARGUE

VILLA QUARTER BASEL

NATURE PARK

KING ESTATE, OREGON, U:S:

NAPA VALLEY ESTATE, U:S:

COUNTRY HOUSE WITH GOLF COURSE, GRUYÈRE

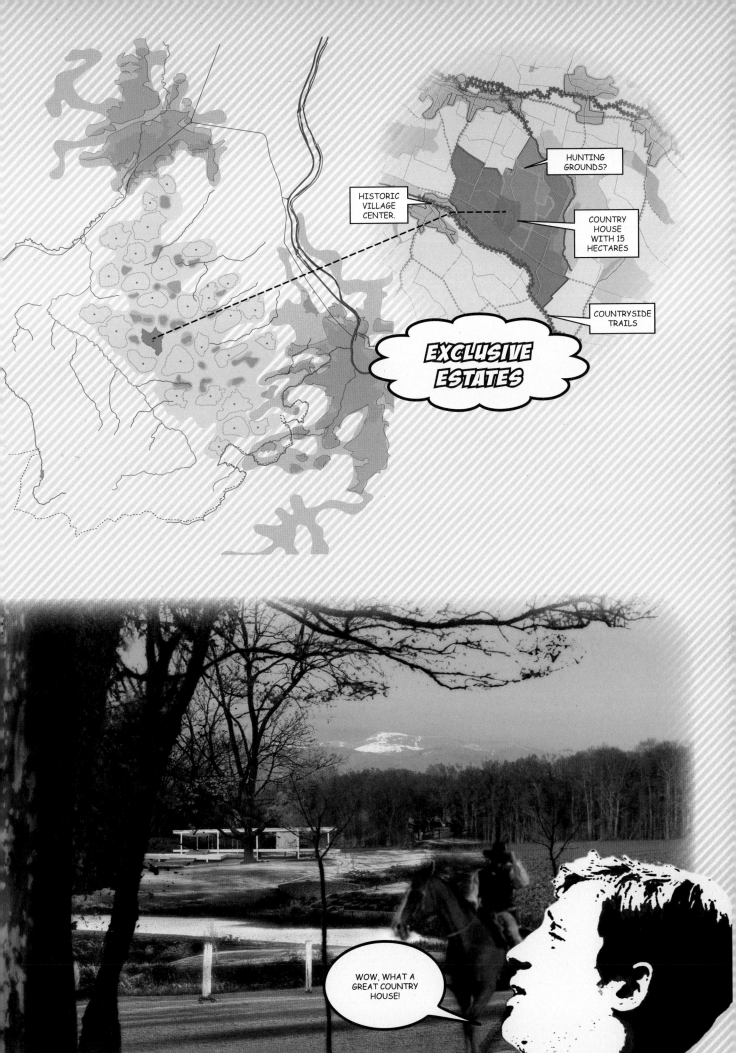

WORKING IN METRO BASEL

METROBASEL IS AN IMPORTANT BUSINESS LOCATION IN EUROPE CONSISTING OF A RANGE OF ECONOMIC SECTORS. THESE SECTORS HAVE SHAPED THE CITY. THEY FORM SPECIFIC SPACES IN THE CITY.

FILIP IS A STUDENT OF ARCHITECTURE AT ETH STUDIO BASEL. HIS RESEARCH INVESTIGATES WORK IN METROBASEL

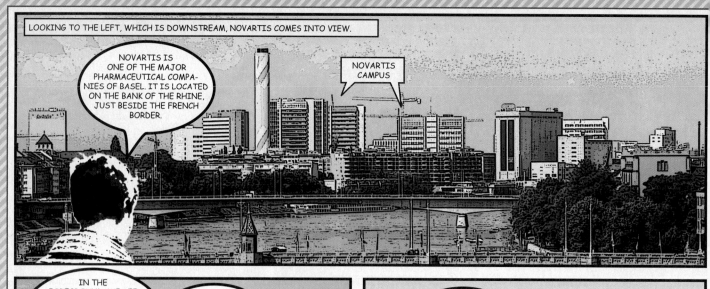

LOOKING TO THE LEFT, WHICH IS DOWNSTREAM, NOVARTIS COMES INTO VIEW.

NOVARTIS IS ONE OF THE MAJOR PHARMACEUTICAL COMPANIES OF BASEL. IT IS LOCATED ON THE BANK OF THE RHINE, JUST BESIDE THE FRENCH BORDER.

NOVARTIS CAMPUS

IN THE FOREGROUND, WE SEE THE MITTLERE BRÜCKE. THERE HAS BEEN A PASSAGE FOR IMPORTANT EUROPEAN BUSINESS ROUTES ACROSS THE RIVER AT THIS LOCATION FOR THOUSANDS OF YEARS.

THAT IS WHY BASEL IS STILL AN IMPORTANT LOGISTICAL CENTER TODAY.

MITTLERE BRÜCKE

THAT IS ALSO BECAUSE OF THE EXHIBITION CENTER, WHICH IS LOCATED IN THE CITY CENTER.

TRADE FAIR TOWER

THEIR GAZE TURNS NORTHEAST OVER THE RHINE...

...AND FURTHER TO THE RIGHT, UPSTREAM.

THE ROCHE COMPOUND

AND HERE WE SEE THE OTHER MAIN PHARMACEUTICAL CORPORATION OF BASEL: ROCHE. IT IS ALSO ON THE RHINE, ALMOST DIRECTLY BY THE CANTONAL BOUNDARY.

I WONDER WHY PHARMACEUTICAL INDUSTRIES ARE ALWAYS BASED ON THE RHINE? AND ALWAYS LOCATED CLOSE TO A BORDER? HMMM... I'D LIKE TO KNOW MORE ABOUT THAT...

INSPIRED BY THE VIEW OF THE VARIOUS INDUSTRIAL AND OFFICE BUILDINGS THAT HE SAW FROM MÜNSTER HILL, MICHEL DECIDES TO GO AND TAKE SOME PICTURES TO CAPTURE THEIR STYLE AND AESTHETICS.

I THINK I MANAGED TO SHOW THE EXTENT TO WHICH WORKPLACES HAVE SHAPED THE CITY IN TERMS OF ARCHITECTURE. LET'S SEE WHAT IT'S LIKE AT THE LEVEL OF URBANISM...

BACK ON SPITALSTRASSE...

PLACES OF WORK IN BASEL: 1) ADMINISTRATIVE BUILDING AUHAFEN; 2) BASEL UNIVERSITY LIBRARY; 3) POLICE HQ PETERSGRABEN; 4) CIBA ADMINISTRATION BUILDING; 5) LONZA ADMINISTRATION BUILDING; 6) TRADE FAIR TOWER HOTEL AND OFFICE BUILDING; 7) AUHAFEN FACTORY AND STOREHOUSE; 8) KLEINHÜNINGEN PORT SILO BUILDING; 9) SCHWEIZERHALLE FACTORY; 10) NOVARTIS CAMPUS ADMINISTRATION; 11) ROCHE RESEARCH AND LAB; 12) NOVARTIS ADMINISTRATION; 13) SCHWEIZERHALLE SILO BUILDING; 14) CIBA ADMINISTRATION; 15) SPITALSTRASSE OFFICE BUILDING.

85

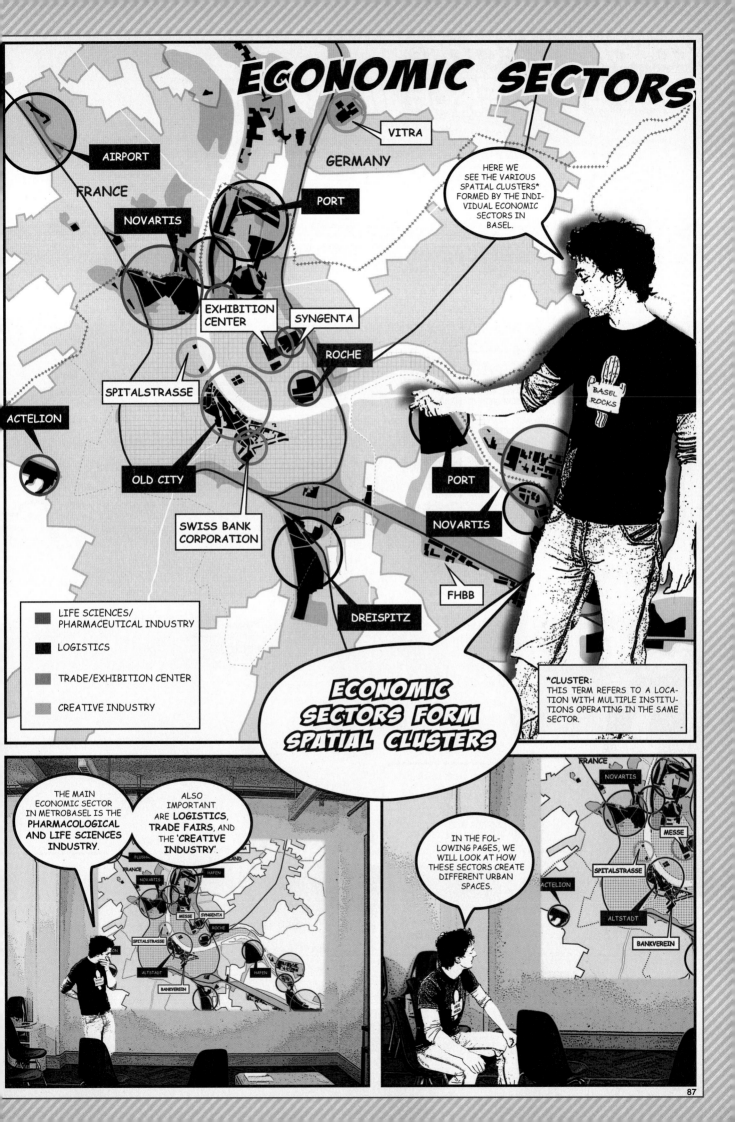

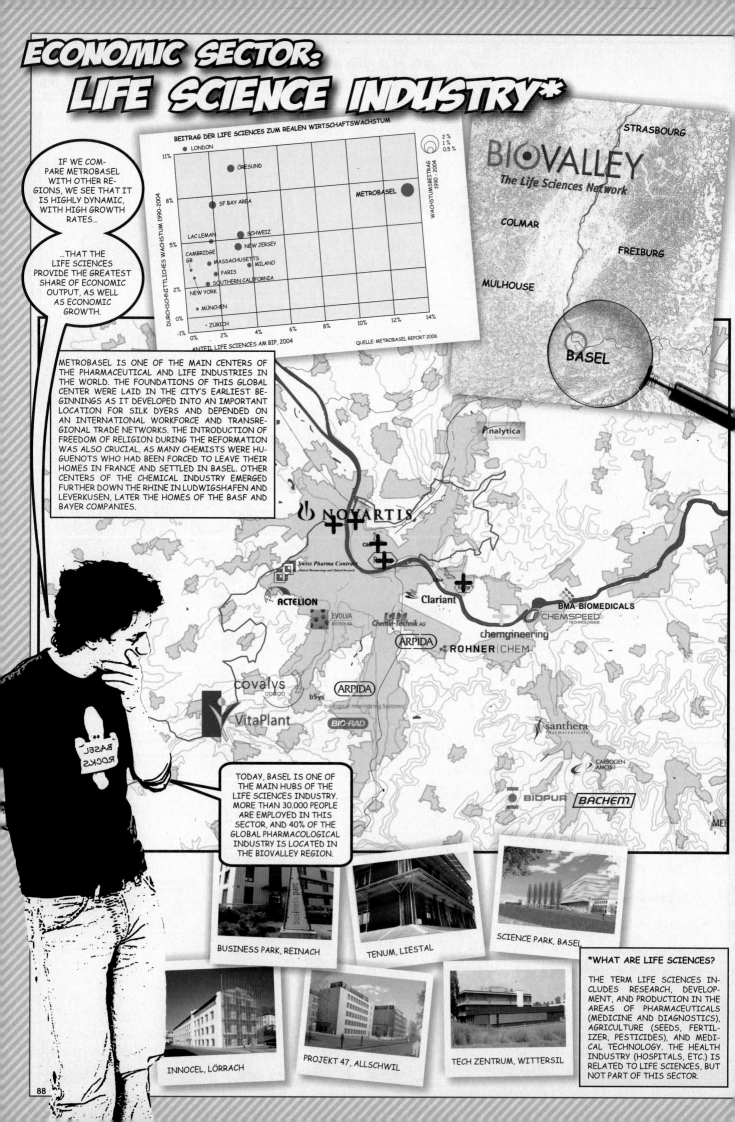

ECONOMIC SECTOR: LIFE SCIENCE INDUSTRY*

BEITRAG DER LIFE SCIENCES ZUM REALEN WIRTSCHAFTSWACHSTUM

WACHSTUMSBEITRAG 1990–2004
2 %
1 %
0.5 %

DURCHSCHNITTLICHES WACHSTUM 1990-2004

- LONDON 11%
- ÖRESUND
- SF BAY AREA 8%
- LAC LEMAN
- SCHWEIZ
- CAMBRIDGE GB 5%
- NEW JERSEY
- MASSACHUSETTS
- PARIS
- MILANO
- SOUTHERN CALIFORNIA
- NEW YORK 2%
- METROBASEL
- MÜNCHEN 0%
- ZÜRICH -1%

ANTEIL LIFE SCIENCES AM BIP, 2004
0% 2% 4% 6% 8% 10% 12% 14%

QUELLE: METROBASEL REPORT 2006

IF WE COMPARE METROBASEL WITH OTHER REGIONS, WE SEE THAT IT IS HIGHLY DYNAMIC, WITH HIGH GROWTH RATES...

...THAT THE LIFE SCIENCES PROVIDE THE GREATEST SHARE OF ECONOMIC OUTPUT, AS WELL AS ECONOMIC GROWTH.

BIOVALLEY
The Life Sciences Network

STRASBOURG
COLMAR
FREIBURG
MULHOUSE
BASEL

METROBASEL IS ONE OF THE MAIN CENTERS OF THE PHARMACEUTICAL AND LIFE INDUSTRIES IN THE WORLD. THE FOUNDATIONS OF THIS GLOBAL CENTER WERE LAID IN THE CITY'S EARLIEST BEGINNINGS AS IT DEVELOPED INTO AN IMPORTANT LOCATION FOR SILK DYERS AND DEPENDED ON AN INTERNATIONAL WORKFORCE AND TRANSREGIONAL TRADE NETWORKS. THE INTRODUCTION OF FREEDOM OF RELIGION DURING THE REFORMATION WAS ALSO CRUCIAL, AS MANY CHEMISTS WERE HUGUENOTS WHO HAD BEEN FORCED TO LEAVE THEIR HOMES IN FRANCE AND SETTLED IN BASEL. OTHER CENTERS OF THE CHEMICAL INDUSTRY EMERGED FURTHER DOWN THE RHINE IN LUDWIGSHAFEN AND LEVERKUSEN, LATER THE HOMES OF THE BASF AND BAYER COMPANIES.

Analytica International

NOVARTIS

Swiss Pharma Contract
Clinical Pharmacology and Clinical Research

Ciba

Clariant

BMA BIOMEDICALS
CHEMSPEED TECHNOLOGIES

ACTELION

EVOLVA BIOTECH SA

Chemie-Technik AG

chemgineering

ARPIDA

ROHNER CHEM

covalys

ARPIDA

bSys
biological monitoring Systems

santhera Pharmaceuticals

VitaPlant

BIO·RAD

CARBOGEN AMCIS

BIOPUR BACHEM

BASEL ROCKS

TODAY, BASEL IS ONE OF THE MAIN HUBS OF THE LIFE SCIENCES INDUSTRY. MORE THAN 30.000 PEOPLE ARE EMPLOYED IN THIS SECTOR, AND 40% OF THE GLOBAL PHARMACOLOGICAL INDUSTRY IS LOCATED IN THE BIOVALLEY REGION.

BUSINESS PARK, REINACH

TENUM, LIESTAL

SCIENCE PARK, BASEL

INNOCEL, LÖRRACH

PROJEKT 47, ALLSCHWIL

TECH ZENTRUM, WITTERSIL

*WHAT ARE LIFE SCIENCES?

THE TERM LIFE SCIENCES INCLUDES RESEARCH, DEVELOPMENT, AND PRODUCTION IN THE AREAS OF PHARMACEUTICALS (MEDICINE AND DIAGNOSTICS), AGRICULTURE (SEEDS, FERTILIZER, PESTICIDES), AND MEDICAL TECHNOLOGY. THE HEALTH INDUSTRY (HOSPITALS, ETC.) IS RELATED TO LIFE SCIENCES, BUT NOT PART OF THIS SECTOR.

THE HISTORY OF THE CHEMICAL INDUSTRY

THE CHEMICAL INDUSTRY ORIGINATED IN THE SILK DYERS' CRAFT: MORE AND MORE COLORS HAD TO BE DEVELOPED IN ORDER TO KEEP PACE WITH FASHION. THEREFORE, SILK DYERS HIRED CHEMISTS TO RESEARCH NEW DYING TECHNIQUES.

THUS, CHEMISTS CAME TO BASEL TO WORK IN THE SILK DYING INDUSTRY AND CONDUCT SCIENTIFIC RESEARCH.

FILIP HAS PREPARED A PRESENTATION ON THE HISTORY OF THE CHEMICAL INDUSTRY – THE PREDECESSOR OF LIFE SCIENCES. IN PARTICULAR, IT DEALS WITH EARLY TRANSREGIONAL ASPECTS AND TRI-NATIONAL ASPECTS OF THIS INDUSTRY.

HELLO!

BONJOUR!

ALEXANDER CLAVEL (1798–1861), ORIGINALLY FROM LYON, PURCHASED KNOW-HOW AND RECIPES FROM THE CHEMISTS WORKING THERE. THE COMPANY LATER BECAME FAMOUS AS CIBA (CHEMISCHE INDUSTRIE IN BASEL).

IN ORDER TO BE ABLE TO COMPETE IN GLOBAL MARKETS, THE METROBASEL REGION TODAY NEEDS WORKERS FROM AN INTERNATIONAL TALENT POOL...

...WHO CONTRIBUTE KNOW-HOW OF THEIR OWN. AS EARLY AS THE 19TH CENTURY, BASEL ATTRACTED SUCH INTERNATIONAL TALENT. THESE WORKERS FORMED THE BASIS FOR THE REGIONAL CHEMICAL INDUSTRY.

GEIGY IN ROSENTAL AROUND 1883

1914 CIBA

INTERNATIONAL TALENT

PRODUCTION FACILITIES ARE LOCATED OUTSIDE THE CENTER AND ACROSS THE BORDER IN GERMANY AND FRANCE.

BASEL ROCKS

CIBA IN KLYBECKSTRASSE

TRINATIONAL HUB

GEIGY IN GRENZACH, GERMANY, 1930

GEIGY IN HUNINGUE, FRANCE

FACTORIES ARE OFTEN LOCATED ALONG THE RHINE, MAKING IT EASIER TO TRANSPORT RAW MATERIAL AND TO DISPOSE OF INDUSTRIAL SEWAGE AND WASTE. DUE TO ODORS AND THE HAZARDS FROM CHEMICALS, PRODUCTION FACILITIES WERE USUALLY BASED NEAR THE BORDER, OUTSIDE OF THE CITY CENTER AND RESIDENTIAL AREAS.

I SEE! BASEL'S LOCATION ON THE RHINE, CLOSE TO POLITICAL, LINGUISTIC, AND RELIGIOUS BOUNDARIES, THE OPEN NATURE OF THE CITY, THE ECONOMIC SITUATION, AND THE CHEMICAL INDUSTRY... THE LARGER PICTURE IS BECOMING CLEARER.

FROM PRODUCTION TO RESEARCH

RESEARCH AND DEVELOPMENT ARE CRUCIAL FOR THE CHEMICAL INDUSTRY.

BASEL DEVELOPED RAPIDLY INTO A HUB OF THE CHEMICAL INDUSTRY IN THE 19TH CENTURY, WITH RESEARCH AND DEVELOPMENT CLOSELY LINKED TO THE PRODUCTION PROCESS.

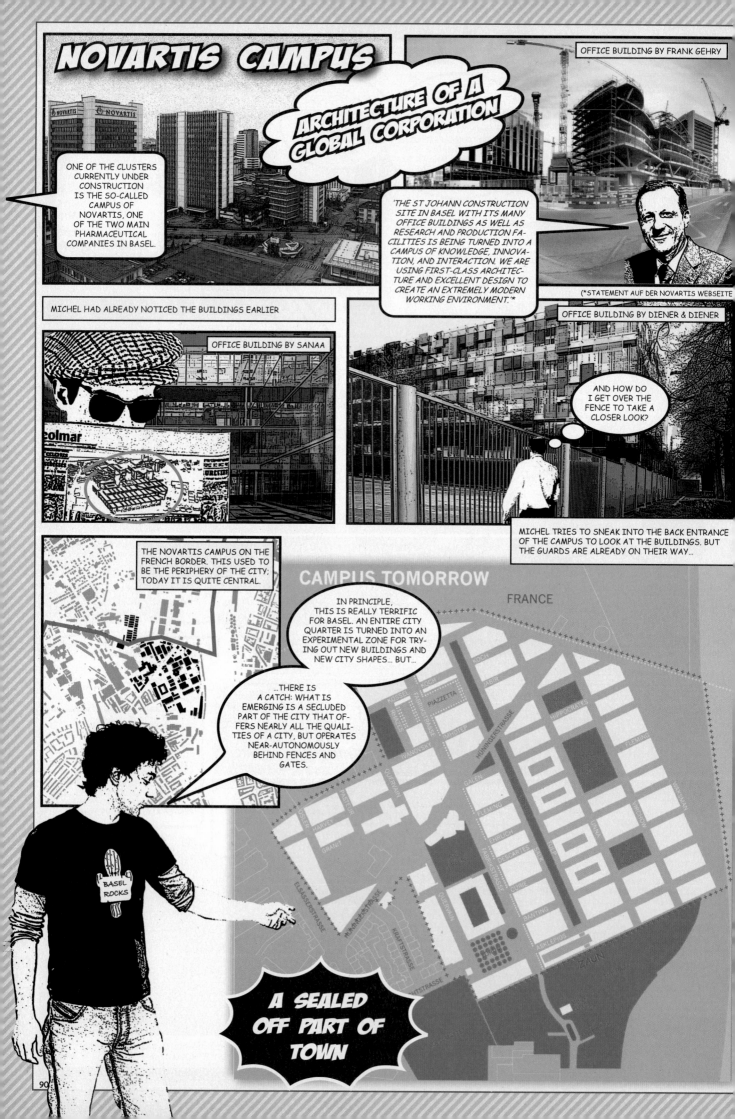

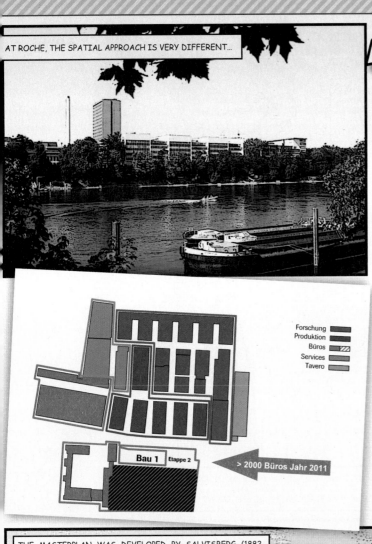

AT ROCHE, THE SPATIAL APPROACH IS VERY DIFFERENT...

Forschung
Produktion
Büros
Services
Tavero

Bau 1 Etappe 2

> 2000 Büros Jahr 2011

ROCHE COMPOUND

„THE WHOLE CITY AS A CAMPUS"

Roche

... BECAUSE WE REGARD OURSELVES AS AN INTEGRAL PART OF THIS CITY AND BELIEVE THAT THIS CITY MUST FUNCTION, THAT IT MUST STAY LIVELY. WE WANT PEOPLE TO MOVE AROUND IN THE URBAN ENVIRONMENT, TO GO OUT TO THE GYM AROUND THE CORNER OR TO THE STORES ON CLARAPLATZ.

M. BALTISBERGER, HEAD OF ROCHE BASEL, IN 'DAS MAGAZIN', 9 MAY 2008.

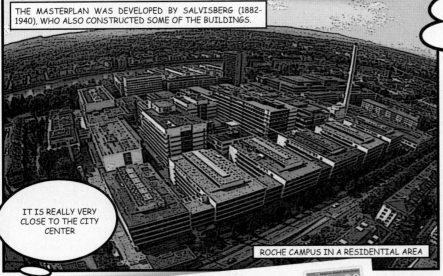

THE MASTERPLAN WAS DEVELOPED BY SALVISBERG (1882-1940), WHO ALSO CONSTRUCTED SOME OF THE BUILDINGS.

IT IS REALLY VERY CLOSE TO THE CITY CENTER

ROCHE CAMPUS IN A RESIDENTIAL AREA

ROCHE IS LOCATED IN THE CENTER OF THE CITY

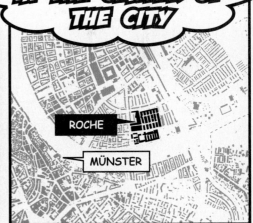

ROCHE

MÜNSTER

ROCHE IN BASEL

Dear Patricia

I really enjoyed the wonderful trip and view of the city with you yesterday... I hope we will be able to get together again in the future.

Big hug
Michel

ECONOMIC SECTOR: LOGISTICS

SINCE THE TIME OF THE CELTS, BASEL HAS BEEN AN INTERSECTION OF TRADE ROUTES WITH A LIVELY FLOW AND EXCHANGE OF GOODS. THE CITY'S LOCATION LAID THE GROUND-WORK FOR ONE OF THE MAIN CENTERS FOR LOGISTICS ON THE CONTINENT: AT ONE OF THE OLDEST RHINE CROSSINGS, AT THE POINT WHERE THE RIVER BECOMES NAVIGABLE AND AT A STRATEGIC LOCATION FOR MANY TRANS-EUROPEAN ROUTES.

INDUSTRIAL-IZATION REINFORCED THESE FACTORS AND ALSO ENHANCED THE ROLE OF BASEL AS A SWISS AND EUROPEAN TRAF-FIC HUB.

BASEL AS A EUROPEAN TRAFFIC HUB

BASEL IS LOCATED ALONG ONE OF THE MOST IMPORTANT NORTH-SOUTH ROUTES THAT TRAVERSE EUROPE AND FACILITATE THE LION'S SHARE OF INTRA-EUROPEAN TRADE AND GOODS.

THE TIMELY COMBINATION OF RAILWAYS, ROADS AND WATERWAYS WAS A DIS-TINGUISHING FEATURE OF THE REGION.

BASEL'S ROLE AS A TRAFFIC HUB MEANT THAT 'INTERMODAL' TRAFFIC, OR THE POSSIBIL-ITY TO CHANGE FROM SHIP TO TRAIN TO TRUCK DEMANDED SEVERE INTRUSION AND INFRASTRUCTURAL MEASURES IN THE REGION: PORTS, CHANNELS, HIGHWAYS, HUMP YARDS, CONTAINER TERMINALS, AND WAREHOUSES.

1832 ARRIVAL OF THE FIRST STEAM SHIP IN BASEL.

TRAFFIC HUB

MODERN TANKER ON THE CHANNELED BRANCH OF THE RHINE

INTERMODAL TRANSPORT OF GOODS: SHIP/RAIL

INTERCITY EXPRESS RAIL LINE TO GERMANY

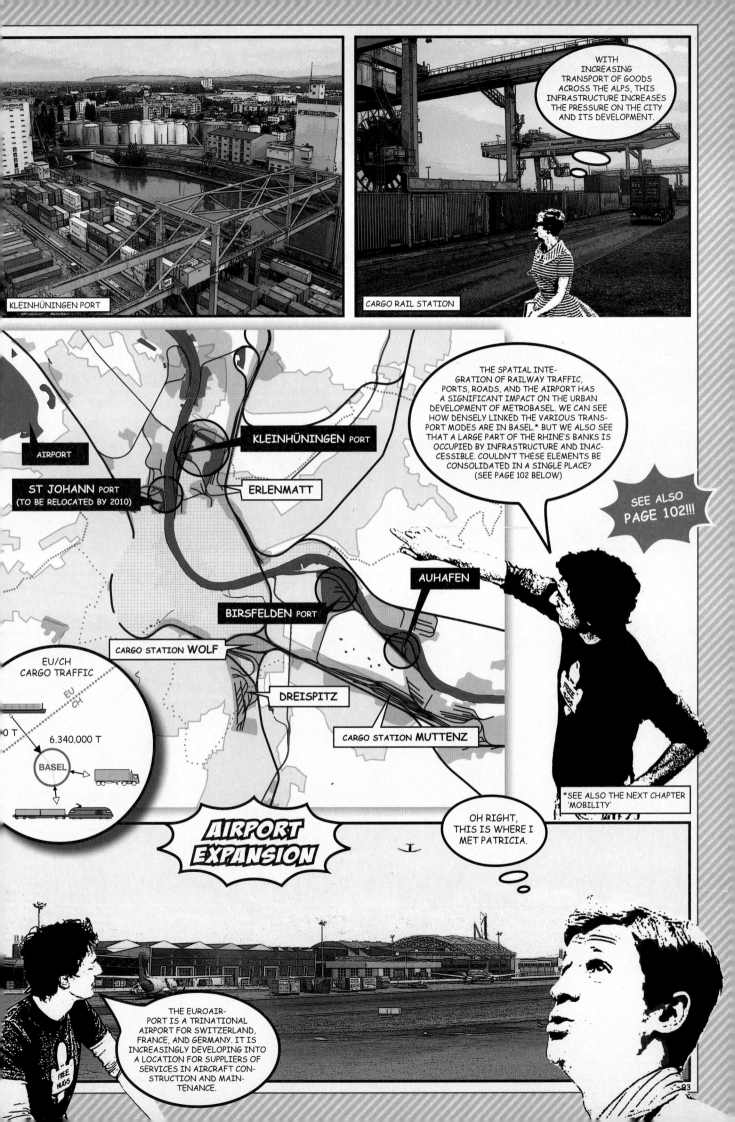

KLEINHÜNINGEN PORT

CARGO RAIL STATION

WITH INCREASING TRANSPORT OF GOODS ACROSS THE ALPS, THIS INFRASTRUCTURE INCREASES THE PRESSURE ON THE CITY AND ITS DEVELOPMENT.

AIRPORT

ST JOHANN PORT
(TO BE RELOCATED BY 2010)

KLEINHÜNINGEN PORT

ERLENMATT

BIRSFELDEN PORT

CARGO STATION WOLF

DREISPITZ

AUHAFEN

CARGO STATION MUTTENZ

THE SPATIAL INTEGRATION OF RAILWAY TRAFFIC, PORTS, ROADS, AND THE AIRPORT HAS A SIGNIFICANT IMPACT ON THE URBAN DEVELOPMENT OF METROBASEL. WE CAN SEE HOW DENSELY LINKED THE VARIOUS TRANSPORT MODES ARE IN BASEL.* BUT WE ALSO SEE THAT A LARGE PART OF THE RHINE'S BANKS IS OCCUPIED BY INFRASTRUCTURE AND INACCESSIBLE. COULDN'T THESE ELEMENTS BE CONSOLIDATED IN A SINGLE PLACE?
(SEE PAGE 102 BELOW)

SEE ALSO PAGE 102!!!

*SEE ALSO THE NEXT CHAPTER 'MOBILITY'

EU/CH CARGO TRAFFIC

EU
CH

O T

6.340.000 T

BASEL

AIRPORT EXPANSION

OH RIGHT, THIS IS WHERE I MET PATRICIA.

THE EUROAIRPORT IS A TRINATIONAL AIRPORT FOR SWITZERLAND, FRANCE, AND GERMANY. IT IS INCREASINGLY DEVELOPING INTO A LOCATION FOR SUPPLIERS OF SERVICES IN AIRCRAFT CONSTRUCTION AND MAINTENANCE.

PERCENTAGE OF FOREIGN VISITORS AND EXHIBITORS ACCORDING TO EXHIBITION CATEGORIES - ANNUAL AVERAGE 2002 TO 2005.

CURRENT STATE OF EXHIBITION CENTER

THE EXHIBITION CENTER AT THE BADISCHER BAHNHOF USED TO BE LOCATED NEAR THE CITY LIMITS. IN THE MEANTIME, THE CITY HAS GROWN AROUND IT. DURING THE SUMMER OF 2008, THERE WAS A HIGHLY CONTROVERSIAL DEBATE OVER WHETHER THE EXHIBITION CENTER WAS TO SPREAD OUT WITHIN THE CITY OR NOT.

1945 "MUSTERMESSE", EXPOSITION OF SAMPLES

INTERNATIONAL CITY

THE LOCATION OF THE EXHIBITION CENTER IN THE HEART OF THE CITY MEANS THAT ITS OPPORTUNITIES FOR GROWTH ARE LIMITED. DOES IT MAKE MORE SENSE TO SHIFT THE ENTIRE CENTER, OR TO CREATE MORE SPACE AT THE CURRENT LOCATION?

IN OTHER CITIES, THE EXHIBITION AREAS ARE USUALLY LOCATED OUTSIDE OF TOWN. BASEL IS ONE OF THE FEW CITIES WHERE THE EXHIBITION AREA IS IN THE CENTER. BUT IT REQUIRES SPACE FOR GROWTH.

EXHIBITION CENTER

CITY

CENTRAL LOCATION IN THE CITY!!!

FINALLY, THE POPULATION DECIDED IN FAVOR OF GROWTH AT THE CURRENT LOCATION. RELOCATING TO THE PERIMETER OF THE CITY WOULD HAVE IMPLIED A SEVERE LOSS OF URBANITY AND INTERNATIONAL FLAIR FOR THE CITY CENTER.

95

ECONOMIC SECTOR: BANKING AND FINANCE

SINCE ITS BEGINNINGS, BASEL HAS ALWAYS BEEN AN IMPORTANT BANKING CITY AND A LOCATION FOR MONEY-LENDERS, STOCK EXCHANGES, AND CAPITAL MARKETS. THE FIRST SWISS BANK WAS FOUNDED HERE. TODAY, HOWEVER, BASEL HAS LARGELY CONCEDED THE ECONOMIC SECTOR TO ZURICH.

NEVERTHELESS, MANY BANK BUILDINGS CONTINUE TO LEAVE THEIR MARK ON THE FACE OF THE CITY.

THE FORMER BUILDING OF THE SWISS BANK CORPORATION

CURRENT LOCATION OF UBS

A SELECTION OF COINS MINTED BY THE CANTON THAT WERE IN USE BEFORE 1805 AND INVALIDATED BY THE REFORM OF 1849/50 SHOW HOW IMPORTANT BASEL WAS FOR THE INTRODUCTION OF THE SWISS FRANC AS A COMMON SWISS CURRENCY.

THE LEGACY OF THE BANKING SECTOR CAN BE SEEN IN THE MANY BUILDINGS FEATURING EXCELLENT ARCHITECTURE.

MICHEL NOTICED THAT MANY OFFICE BUILDINGS IN TOWN LOOK QUITE INTERESTING...

THIS IS CREDIT SUISSE WITH AN INSTALLATION BY KLAUS LITTMANN

THIS IS THE UBS TRAINING CENTER BY DIENER & DIENER

THE FINANCE SECTOR AS AN ENGINE OF ARCHITECTURE

INSURANCE BUILDING BY DIENER & DIENER

BANK FOR INTERNATIONAL SETTLEMENTS

WOW, GREAT BUILDINGS! YOU CAN SEE HOW THE FINANCIAL SECTOR FOSTERED A CULTURE OF CONSTRUCTION AND HELPED TO SHAPE THE APPEARANCE OF THE CITY.

ALSO BANK FOR INTERNATIONAL SETTLEMENTS TODAY

THIS USED TO BE THE UBS BUILDING. ARCHITECT: MARIO BOTTA!

IN FRONT OF THE UBS BANK BUILDING BY PETER MÄRKLI

ECONOMIC SECTOR: THE CREATIVE INDUSTRIES*

THE CREATIVE INDUSTRIES OFTEN ADOPT THE STRUCTURAL SHAPE OF A CLUSTER WITHIN A CITY. A GOOD EXAMPLE OF THIS IS THE VITRA CAMPUS IN WEIL.

IT BRINGS TOGETHER SOME OF THE BEST BUILDINGS AND ARCHITECTS IN THE WORLD.

*THE 'CREATIVE INDUSTRIES' ARE COMPANIES AND AGENCIES ACTIVE IN THE FIELDS OF ARCHITECTURE, DESIGN, FURNITURE, ADVERTISING, AND ART.

VITRA CAMPUS

CREATIVE INDUSTRIES

CONFERENCE CENTER BY TADAO ANDO

THE VITRA CAMPUS CERTAINLY CONSTITUTES ONE OF THE MOST UNUSUAL WORKPLACES IN THE REGION.

FIREHOUSE BY ZAHA HADID

THE BRIDGE BETWEEN FACTORY BUILDING BY NICHOLAS GRIMSHAW (LEFT) AND ALVARO SIZA (RIGHT) WITH THE FIREHOUSE BY ZAHA HADID (BACKGROUND)

FACTORY BUILDING BY NICHOLAS GRIMSHAW

I HAVE TO SHOW MICHEL ALL OF THIS...

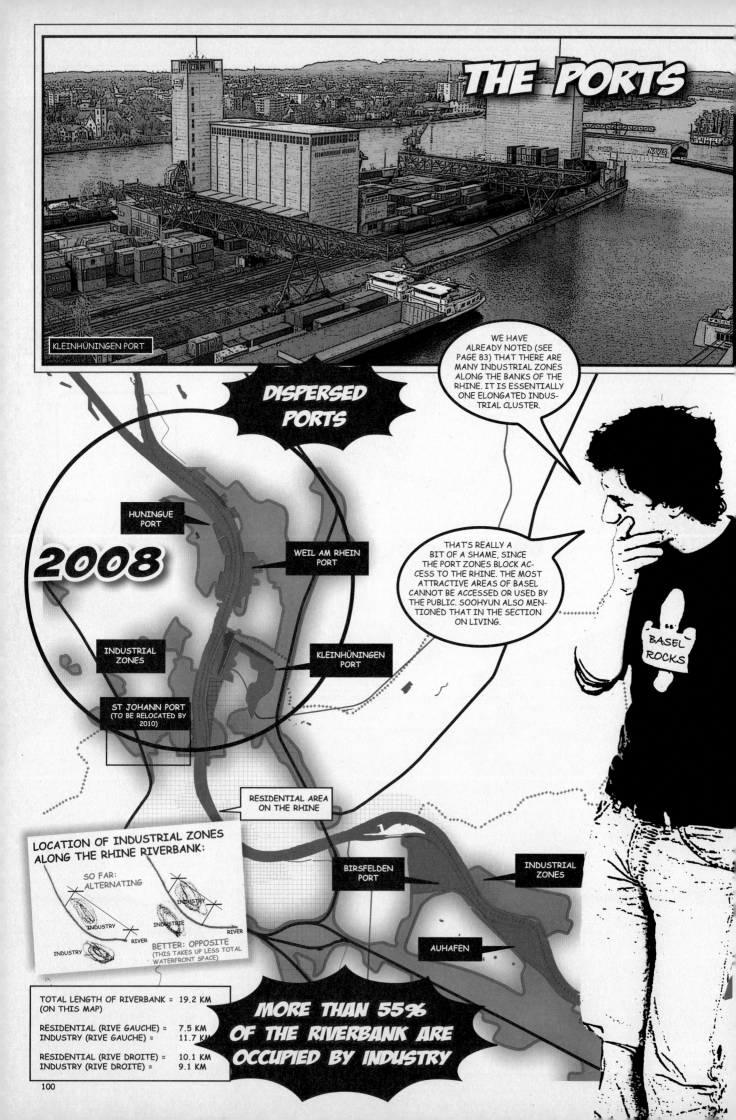

THE PORTS

KLEINHÜNINGEN PORT

DISPERSED PORTS

WE HAVE ALREADY NOTED (SEE PAGE 83) THAT THERE ARE MANY INDUSTRIAL ZONES ALONG THE BANKS OF THE RHINE. IT IS ESSENTIALLY ONE ELONGATED INDUSTRIAL CLUSTER.

2008

HUNINGUE PORT

WEIL AM RHEIN PORT

THAT'S REALLY A BIT OF A SHAME, SINCE THE PORT ZONES BLOCK ACCESS TO THE RHINE. THE MOST ATTRACTIVE AREAS OF BASEL CANNOT BE ACCESSED OR USED BY THE PUBLIC. SOOHYUN ALSO MENTIONED THAT IN THE SECTION ON LIVING.

INDUSTRIAL ZONES

KLEINHÜNINGEN PORT

ST JOHANN PORT (TO BE RELOCATED BY 2010)

BASEL ROCKS

RESIDENTIAL AREA ON THE RHINE

LOCATION OF INDUSTRIAL ZONES ALONG THE RHINE RIVERBANK:

SO FAR: ALTERNATING

INDUSTRY

INDUSTRY

RIVER

INDUSTRY

INDUSTRIE

RIVER

BETTER: OPPOSITE (THIS TAKES UP LESS TOTAL WATERFRONT SPACE)

RIVER

BIRSFELDEN PORT

INDUSTRIAL ZONES

AUHAFEN

TOTAL LENGTH OF RIVERBANK = 19.2 KM (ON THIS MAP)

RESIDENTIAL (RIVE GAUCHE) = 7.5 KM
INDUSTRY (RIVE GAUCHE) = 11.7 KM

RESIDENTIAL (RIVE DROITE) = 10.1 KM
INDUSTRY (RIVE DROITE) = 9.1 KM

MORE THAN 55% OF THE RIVERBANK ARE OCCUPIED BY INDUSTRY

2008

WOULD IT BE CONCEIVABLE TO HAVE A SINGLE PORT INSTEAD OF THE MANY DIFFERENT PORTS? WE COULD RELOCATE THE ENTIRE 175 HECTARES IN THE NORTHERN PART OF METROBASEL.

THE RHINE PORT, HUNINGUE, FRANCE

BIRSFELDEN PORT

AUHAFEN, MUTTENZ

ST JOHANN PORT

A PORT FOR THE ENTIRE METROBASEL REGION NORTH OF THE NUCLEATED CITY WOULD HAVE THE ADVANTAGE OF BEING IDEALLY LINKED TO TRAFFIC INFRASTRUCTURE AND MORE EFFICIENT.

WHAT IF....?

POSSIBLE LOCATION OF NEW METROBASEL PORT

RAIL AND HIGHWAY LINK

CONNECTION TO EUROAIRPORT

POSSIBLE LOCATION OF NEW METROBASEL PORT

2038

CURRENT STATE

RHINE PORT, KLEINHÜNINGEN

NEW CITY QUARTER

LIVING NEAR THE WATER

ONE OF THE OLD INDUSTRIAL ZONES THAT WILL BE REUSED IN THE VERY NEAR FUTURE IS THE HARBOR COMPOUND NORTH OF THE CORE CITY.

A NEW TRI-NATIONAL CITY QUARTER

NOVARTIS

NEW PEDESTRIAN BRIDGE

F

RESIDENTIAL AREA

"DREILÄNDERECK" THREE-COUNTRY CORNER

MOVING IN METRO BASEL

> BASEL IS A CITY WHERE MOBILITY AND TRANSPORT OF GOODS AND PEOPLE IS OF PARAMOUNT IMPORTANCE. TRAFFIC AND INFRASTRUCTURE HAVE DETERMINED THE SHAPE OF THE CITY SINCE ITS EARLIEST BEGINNINGS.

HERE, WE MEET TWO FRIENDS OF PATRICIA WHO ARE QUITE THE EXPERTS IN THE TOPIC OF 'MOVING' IN METROBASEL: ERIK (LEFT) AND FRANCIS (RIGHT).

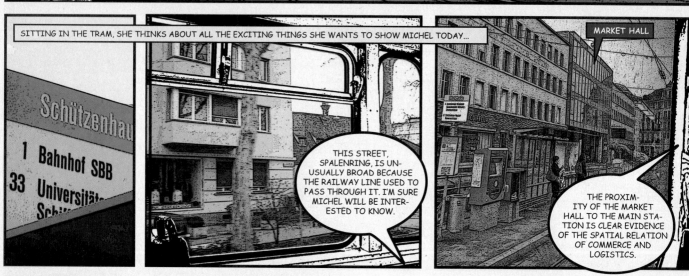

113

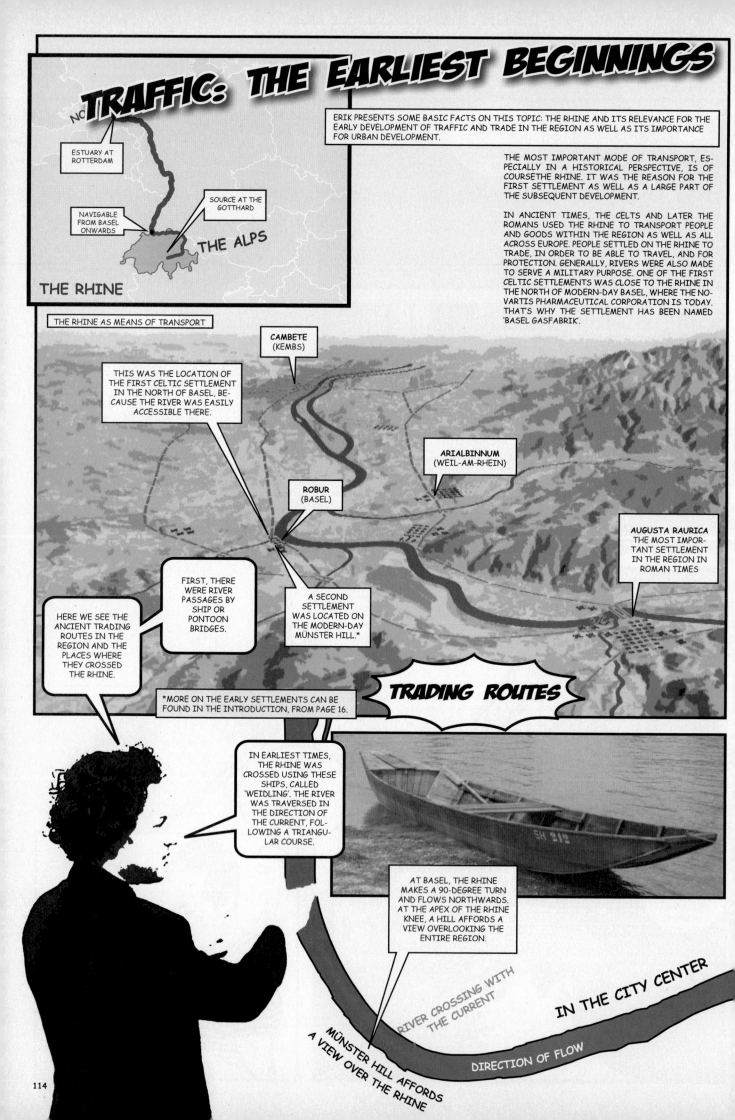

HERE WE SEE THE OLDEST DEPICTION OF BASEL OF 1356. IT SHOWS MITTLERE BRÜCKE AND CITY QUARTERS ON BOTH SIDES OF THE RHINE.

GROSS-BASEL

KLEIN-BASEL

MITTLERE BRÜCKE

IN 1255, THE FIRST PERMA-NENT BRIDGE WAS CON-STRUCTED....

...ON THE EXACT SPOT WHERE MITTLERE BRÜCKE STANDS TODAY.

THE FOUNDATION OF CONTEMPORARY KLEINBASEL IS DIRECTLY LINKED TO THE CONSTRUC-TION OF MITTLERE BRÜCKE.

IN ORDER FOR A SETTLE-MENT TO SECURE ITS AREA OF INFLUENCE, IT IS CRUCIAL THAT IT SHOULD CONTROL BOTH BANKS OF THE RIVER. IN ADDITION TO MILITARY ADVANTAGES - ALLOWING THE ESTABLISHMENT OF DEFENSIVE PERIMETERS IN ALL DIRECTIONS, OF-FERING MORE OPTIONS FOR RETREAT, AND DIS-RUPTING THE EFFORTS OF POTENTIAL ENEMIES TO CROSS THE RIVER - THERE ARE ALSO FINANCIAL AD-VANTAGES: IT WAS MUCH EASIER THIS WAY TO LEVY A ROAD TAX AND CONTROL THE FLOW OF GOODS.

THIS IS TRUE, ON THE ONE HAND, FOR GOODS TRANSPORTED BY RIVER, BUT ALSO FOR GOODS CARRIED ALONG TRANSPORT ROUTES CROSSING THE RIVER BY BRIDGE.

MITTLERE BRÜCKE

WHEN THE BRIDGE WAS BUILT, THE BISHOP OF BASEL PURCHASED A TRACT OF LAND FROM HIS COL-LEAGUE IN CONSTANCE. THESE WERE THE BEGINNINGS OF KLEINBASEL AND THE BOR-OUGH OF RIEHEN.

BASEL

THE MODEL OF A CITY STRADDLING TWO RIVER BANKS, CONNECTED BY A BRIDGE, IS PROBABLY ONE OF THE MOST IMPORTANT URBAN MODELS IN EUROPE. THIS SETTLEMENT PATTERN CAN BE FOUND IN ROMAN CITIES SUCH AS COLOGNE, MAINZ, OR KOBLENZ.

UNIFICATION OF SWITZERLAND

WOW!! MITTLERE BRÜCKE WAS SIGNIFICANT NOT ONLY FOR TRANSPORT OF GOODS, BUT ALSO FOR THE FOUNDATION OF SWITZERLAND!*

THE MITTLERE BRÜCKE IS LINKED TO THE DEVIL'S BRIDGE ON THE ST GOTTHARD PASS. THIS FACILITATED THE ESTABLISHMENT OF TRANSCONTINENTAL TRADE ROUTES ACROSS THE ALPS.

1225 MITTLERE BRÜCKE

1291 RÜTLI OATH

1198 TEUFFELSBRÜCKE GOTTHARD PASS

THE RÜTLI IS A MOUNTAIN MEADOW SITUATED NEAR LAKE LUCERNE, BESIDE THE ALPINE ROUTE CONNECTING MITTLERE BRÜCKE AND THE DEVIL'S BRIDGE. ACCORDING TO LEGEND, THIS IS WHERE THE FOUNDING CANTONS DECLARED THEIR SOLEMN OATH OF ALLIANCE IN 1291.

KEY EVENTS IN SWISS HISTORY

MITTLERE BRÜCKE IN THE 19TH CENTURY; AT THE TIME, IT WAS PARTLY WOODEN AND PARTLY BUILT OF STONE.

DUE TO THE CURRENT AND GREATER DEPTH OF THE RIVER, THE GROSSBASEL SIDE OF THE BRIDGE WAS CONSTRUCTED FROM WOOD. ON THE KLEINBASEL SIDE, THE LESSER CURRENT MADE A STONE CONSTRUCTION POSSIBLE.

MITTLERE BRÜCKE TODAY

WOW, COOL! THIS REALLY IS A HISTORIC BRIDGE.

115

WHILE THE RIVER WAS THE MAIN MEANS OF TRANSPORT THAT SHAPED BASEL IN ANTIQUITY AND THE MIDDLE AGES, A COMPLETELY NEW WAY OF TRAVELLING WAS ADDED DURING THE AGE OF INDUSTRIALIZATION THAT WAS TO ALTER THE CITY IN FUNDAMENTAL WAYS: THE RAILWAY!

...THE FIRST TRAIN OF THE ALSATIAN RAILWAYS ARRIVED IN BASEL ON 15 JUNE 1844.

ONE YEAR LATER, THE FIRST RAILWAY STATION WITHIN THE CITY WALLS WAS CONSTRUCTED. BASEL WAS THE FIRST SWISS CITY TO BE LINKED TO THE NEW MEANS OF TRANSPORT.

GERMANY

FRANCE

ST JOHANN STATION

TEMPORARY STATION (ENGELGASSE/ LANGE GASSE)

THE FIRST RAILWAY IN SWITZERLAND !!!!

1850

CITY GATE

IN THE EARLY YEARS, THERE WAS A SPECIAL GATE IN THE CITY WALL FOR THE RAILWAY. TRAINS WOULD PASS THROUGH IT INTO THE CITY, AND IT WAS ALWAYS CLOSED FOR THE NIGHT.

DEDICATION OF ST JOHANN RAILWAY STATION ON 11 DECEMBER 1845

BESIDES SHIPPING, THE RAILWAY IS THE MEANS OF TRANSPORT THAT HAS BEEN THE MOST IN-FLUENTIAL IN THE CITY'S DEVELOPMENT.

THE LOCATION OF THE VERY FIRST RAILROAD TRACKS AND STATIONS STILL STRONGLY SHAPES THE COMPOSITION OF THE CITY, ITS POTENTIAL FOR DEVELOPMENT, AND THE IN-TERCONNECTION BETWEEN DIFFERENT PARTS OF THE CITY. THIS IS TRUE NOT ONLY FOR BASEL, BUT ESSENTIALLY APPLIES TO ALMOST EVERY CITY. ONCE THE TRACKS HAVE BEEN LAID DOWN, THEIR COURSE IS AL-MOST NEVER CHANGED.

THE HISTORY OF THE RAILWAY

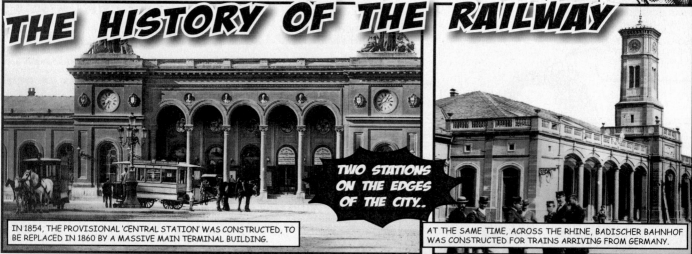

TWO STATIONS ON THE EDGES OF THE CITY..

IN 1854, THE PROVISIONAL 'CENTRAL STATION' WAS CONSTRUCTED, TO BE REPLACED IN 1860 BY A MASSIVE MAIN TERMINAL BUILDING.

AT THE SAME TIME, ACROSS THE RHINE, BADISCHER BAHNHOF WAS CONSTRUCTED FOR TRAINS ARRIVING FROM GERMANY.

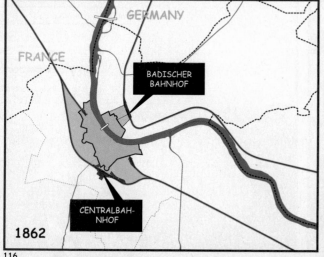

GERMANY

FRANCE

BADISCHER BAHNHOF

CENTRALBAH-NHOF

1862

...BUT NO STATION IN THE CITY CENTER!

BADISCHER BAHNHOF

CENTRALBAHN-HOF, BUILT 1865

SCHWARZWALDBRÜCKE, 1870

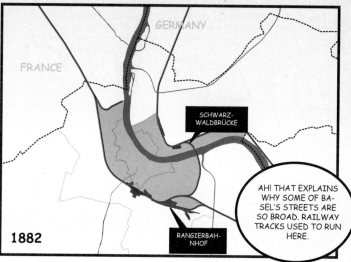

GERMANY

FRANCE

SCHWARZ-WALDBRÜCKE

RANGIERBAH-NHOF

1882

AH! THAT EXPLAINS WHY SOME OF BA-SEL'S STREETS ARE SO BROAD. RAILWAY TRACKS USED TO RUN HERE.

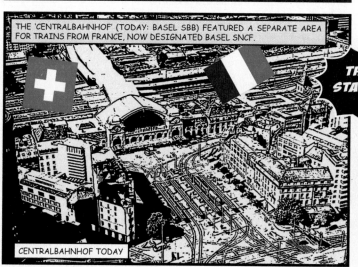

THE 'CENTRALBAHNHOF' (TODAY: BASEL SBB) FEATURED A SEPARATE AREA FOR TRAINS FROM FRANCE, NOW DESIGNATED BASEL SNCF.

CENTRALBAHNHOF TODAY

THREE STATIONS

BADISCHER BAHNHOF, 1913

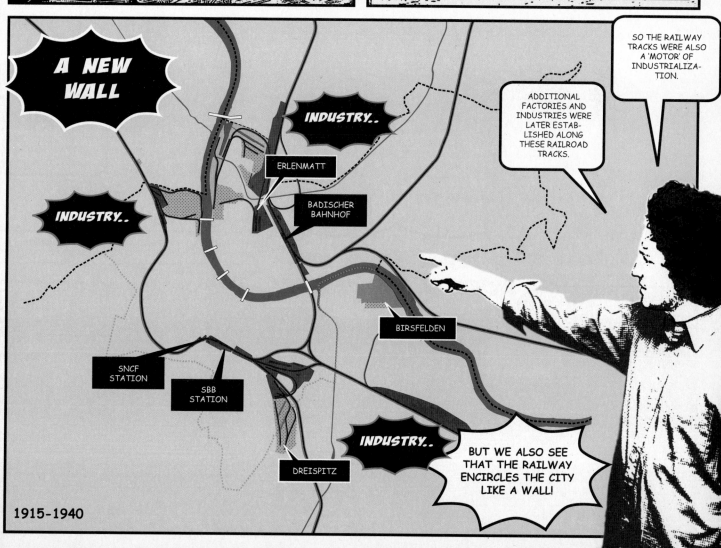

A NEW WALL

INDUSTRY..

ERLENMATT

INDUSTRY..

BADISCHER BAHNHOF

SO THE RAILWAY TRACKS WERE ALSO A 'MOTOR' OF INDUSTRIALIZA-TION.

ADDITIONAL FACTORIES AND INDUSTRIES WERE LATER ESTAB-LISHED ALONG THESE RAILROAD TRACKS.

BIRSFELDEN

SNCF STATION

SBB STATION

INDUSTRY..

DREISPITZ

BUT WE ALSO SEE THAT THE RAILWAY ENCIRCLES THE CITY LIKE A WALL!

1915-1940

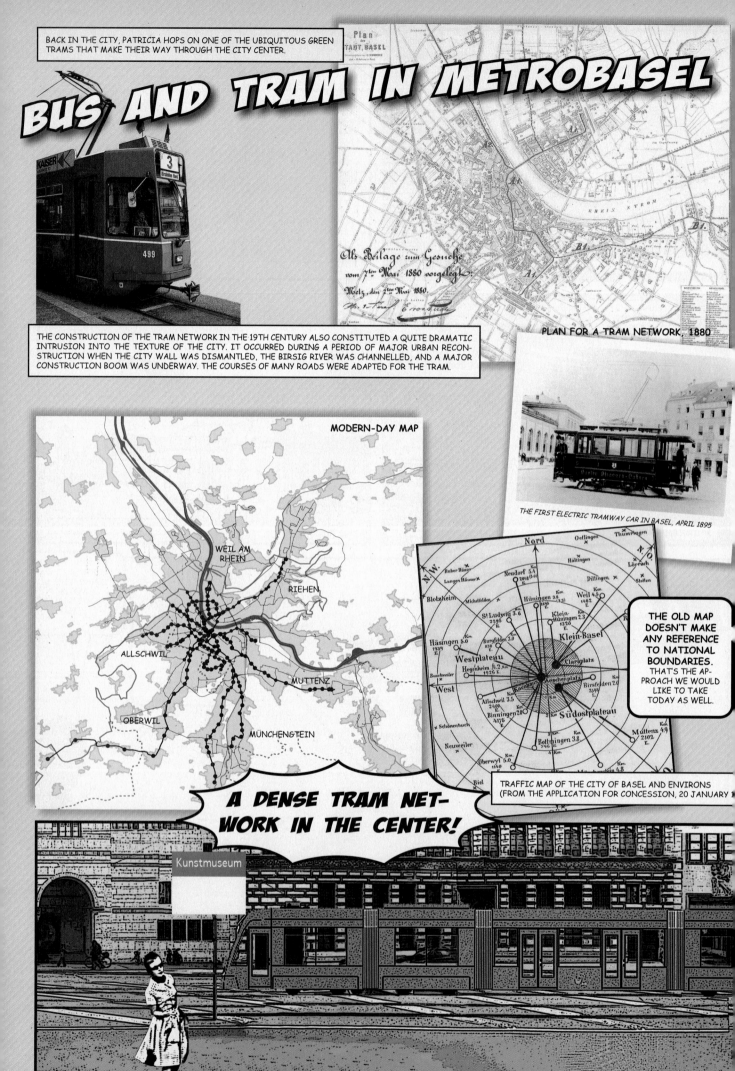

BACK IN THE CITY, PATRICIA HOPS ON ONE OF THE UBIQUITOUS GREEN TRAMS THAT MAKE THEIR WAY THROUGH THE CITY CENTER.

BUS AND TRAM IN METROBASEL

PLAN FOR A TRAM NETWORK, 1880

THE CONSTRUCTION OF THE TRAM NETWORK IN THE 19TH CENTURY ALSO CONSTITUTED A QUITE DRAMATIC INTRUSION INTO THE TEXTURE OF THE CITY. IT OCCURRED DURING A PERIOD OF MAJOR URBAN RECONSTRUCTION WHEN THE CITY WALL WAS DISMANTLED, THE BIRSIG RIVER WAS CHANNELLED, AND A MAJOR CONSTRUCTION BOOM WAS UNDERWAY. THE COURSES OF MANY ROADS WERE ADAPTED FOR THE TRAM.

MODERN-DAY MAP

WEIL AM RHEIN

RIEHEN

ALLSCHWIL

MUTTENZ

OBERWIL

MÜNCHENSTEIN

THE FIRST ELECTRIC TRAMWAY CAR IN BASEL, APRIL 1895

THE OLD MAP DOESN'T MAKE ANY REFERENCE TO NATIONAL BOUNDARIES. THAT'S THE APPROACH WE WOULD LIKE TO TAKE TODAY AS WELL.

TRAFFIC MAP OF THE CITY OF BASEL AND ENVIRONS (FROM THE APPLICATION FOR CONCESSION, 20 JANUARY

A DENSE TRAM NETWORK IN THE CENTER!

Kunstmuseum

118

MICHEL WANTS TO TRY HOW IT FEELS TO TRAVEL BY TRAM AT LEAST ACROSS THE CANTONAL BORDERS AND HEADS TO BASEL-COUNTRY...

NOW I'M IN BASEL-COUNTRY, AND YOU COULDN'T TELL WHERE THE CANTONAL BOUNDARY WAS.

PATRICIA HAS A MUCH HARDER TIME CROSSING THE NATIONAL BORDER BY PUBLIC TRANSPORT...

3 COUNTRIES 4 SYSTEMS

OH BOY! THIS IS A PAIN. CAN ANYBODY FIGURE THIS OUT? PLUS, THEY ONLY RUN ONCE IN A BLUE MOON. GRRRR.

HOW ARE YOU SUP-POSED TO MAKE HEADS OR TAILS OF THIS? THE MAPS AND TICKETS OF THE THREE SYSTEMS ARE ALL DIFFERENT.

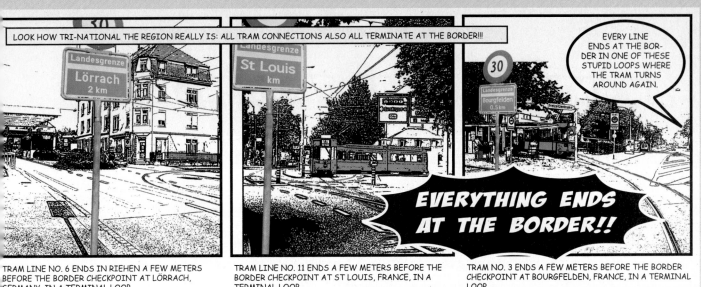

LOOK HOW TRI-NATIONAL THE REGION REALLY IS: ALL TRAM CONNECTIONS ALSO ALL TERMINATE AT THE BORDER!!!

EVERY LINE ENDS AT THE BORDER IN ONE OF THESE STUPID LOOPS WHERE THE TRAM TURNS AROUND AGAIN.

EVERYTHING ENDS AT THE BORDER!!

TRAM LINE NO. 6 ENDS IN RIEHEN A FEW METERS BEFORE THE BORDER CHECKPOINT AT LÖRRACH, GERMANY, IN A TERMINAL LOOP.

TRAM LINE NO. 11 ENDS A FEW METERS BEFORE THE BORDER CHECKPOINT AT ST LOUIS, FRANCE, IN A TERMINAL LOOP.

TRAM NO. 3 ENDS A FEW METERS BEFORE THE BORDER CHECKPOINT AT BOURGFELDEN, FRANCE, IN A TERMINAL LOOP.

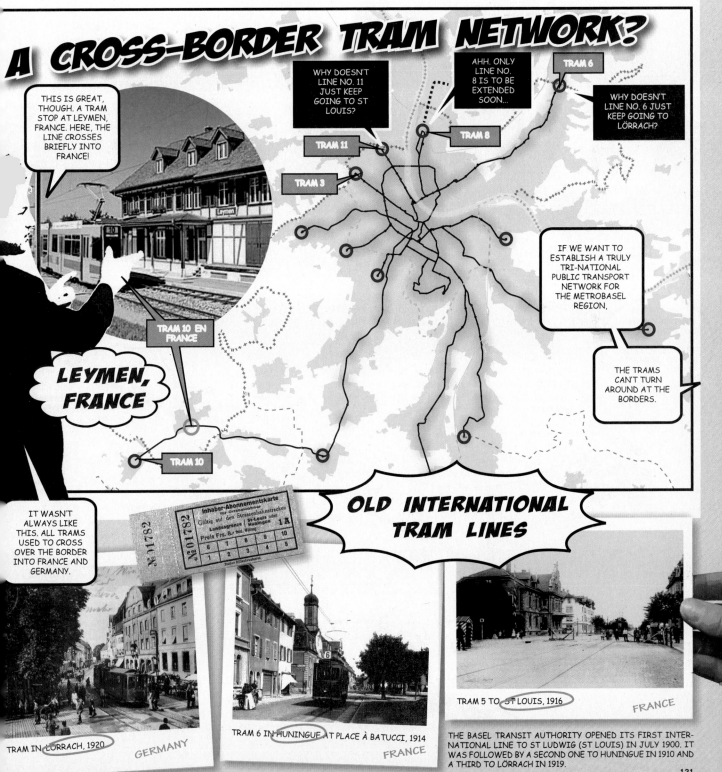

A CROSS-BORDER TRAM NETWORK?

THIS IS GREAT, THOUGH. A TRAM STOP AT LEYMEN, FRANCE. HERE, THE LINE CROSSES BRIEFLY INTO FRANCE!

WHY DOESN'T LINE NO. 11 JUST KEEP GOING TO ST LOUIS?

AHH. ONLY LINE NO. 8 IS TO BE EXTENDED SOON...

WHY DOESN'T LINE NO. 6 JUST KEEP GOING TO LÖRRACH?

TRAM 6

TRAM 8

TRAM 11

TRAM 3

IF WE WANT TO ESTABLISH A TRULY TRI-NATIONAL PUBLIC TRANSPORT NETWORK FOR THE METROBASEL REGION,

TRAM 10 EN FRANCE

LEYMEN, FRANCE

THE TRAMS CAN'T TURN AROUND AT THE BORDERS.

TRAM 10

OLD INTERNATIONAL TRAM LINES

IT WASN'T ALWAYS LIKE THIS. ALL TRAMS USED TO CROSS OVER THE BORDER INTO FRANCE AND GERMANY.

TRAM IN LÖRRACH, 1920
GERMANY

TRAM 6 IN HUNINGUE AT PLACE À BATUCCI, 1914
FRANCE

TRAM 5 TO ST LOUIS, 1916
FRANCE

THE BASEL TRANSIT AUTHORITY OPENED ITS FIRST INTERNATIONAL LINE TO ST LUDWIG (ST LOUIS) IN JULY 1900. IT WAS FOLLOWED BY A SECOND ONE TO HUNINGUE IN 1910 AND A THIRD TO LÖRRACH IN 1919.

AN INTERNATIONAL TRAM NETWORK

AS PATRICIA IS SITTING IN THE TRAM, SHE THROWS A GLANCE AT AN ADVERTISEMENT FOR AN AIRLINE OFFERING FLIGHTS FROM BASEL TO DESTINATIONS ALL ACROSS EUROPE. THE AIRPORT OF THE METROBASEL REGION IS CALLED EUROAIRPORT. IT IS LOCATED IN THE FRENCH PART AND EASY TO ACCESS BY A NUMBER OF AIRLINES.

IT'S NICE THAT BASEL IS SO WELL CONNECTED WITH THE REST OF EUROPE. ONLY THING IS THAT IT'S NOT ALWAYS SO EASY TO GET TO THE AIRPORT...

AND WHAT ABOUT A DIRECT FLIGHT TO NEW YORK?

I JUST WANTED TO TELL YOU HOW NICE IT IS TO DISCOVER THE CITY WITH YOU (EVEN IF THE CONNECTIONS ARE SOMETIMES VERY DIFFICULT).

I HOPE YOU LIKE THE PICTURE.

GRÜSSLI AUS BASEL

AT FIRST GLANCE, IT SEEMS AS IF EVERYTHING WERE WELL CONNECTED... BUT...

THE DIS-CONNECTED CENTER!

... BUT WE CAN HARDLY GET TO THE CENTER FROM THE SURROUNDING AREA...

... OR FROM LÖRRACH TO ST LOUIS.

SINCE THERE IS NO RAILWAY STATION IN CITY CENTER, THE DOWNTOWN AREA IS NOT DIRECTLY CONNECTED WITH THE SURROUNDING REGION OF METROBASEL. IF YOU WANT TO TRAVEL FROM LÖRRACH TO THE BASEL MARKETPLACE, YOU HAVE TO TAKE THE URBAN RAILWAY TO BADISCHER BAHNHOF AND CHANGE TO THE TRAM THERE. THIS MEANS THAT THE RIDE TAKES 20 MINUTES LONGER THAN NECESSARY.** SO IT'S DIFFICULT FOR REGION TO MAKE GOOD USE OF THE CITY CENTER. BUT IF WE WANT TO REGARD METROBASEL AS AN INTEGRATED TRI-NATIONAL REGION, IT IS ESPECIALLY IMPORTANT FOR THE SURROUNDING COUNTRYSIDE THAT THE CITY CENTER SHOULD BE EASILY ACCESSIBLE. OTHERWISE, THE REGION WILL REMAIN FRAGMENTED OR, EVEN WORSE, THE CITY CENTER WILL BECOME DESERTED.

BUT THIS IS NOT JUST ABOUT CONNECTING THE CITY CENTER AND THE REGION; IT IS ALSO ABOUT LINKING THE VARIOUS PARTS OF THE REGION BETTER. IT MUST BE POSSIBLE TO TRAVEL QUICKLY FROM THE GERMAN PART OF METROBASEL TO THE FRENCH PART, OR TO REACH THE AIRPORT DIRECTLY, OR TO TRAVEL QUICKLY FROM BASEL-COUNTRY TO LÖRRACH. TO THIS END, WE MUST CLOSELY INTEGRATE THE TWO RAILWAY STATIONS OF BASEL SBB AND BADISCHER BAHNHOF ACROSS THE DOWNTOWN AREA. BUT HOW?

FROM THIS PERSPECTIVE, LOOKING AT THE REGION FROM ABOVE, WE MIGHT THINK THAT THE VARIOUS PARTS ARE WELL INTEGRATED. BUT WITH ONE EXCEPTION...

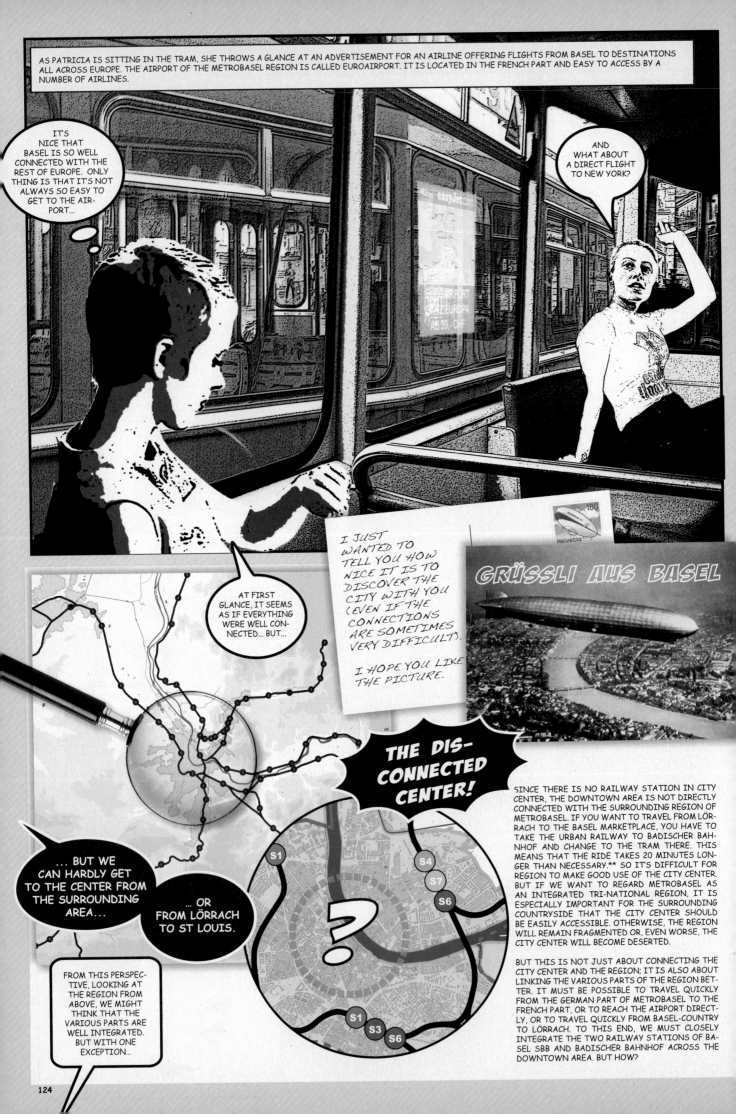

** SEE ALSO THE 'HERZSTÜCK' STUDY BY THE CANTONS OF BASEL-CITY AND BASEL-COUNTRY AS WELL AS THE SBB, WHICH WAS UNDERTAKEN IN COLLABORATION WITH ETH STUDIO BASEL IN 2004.

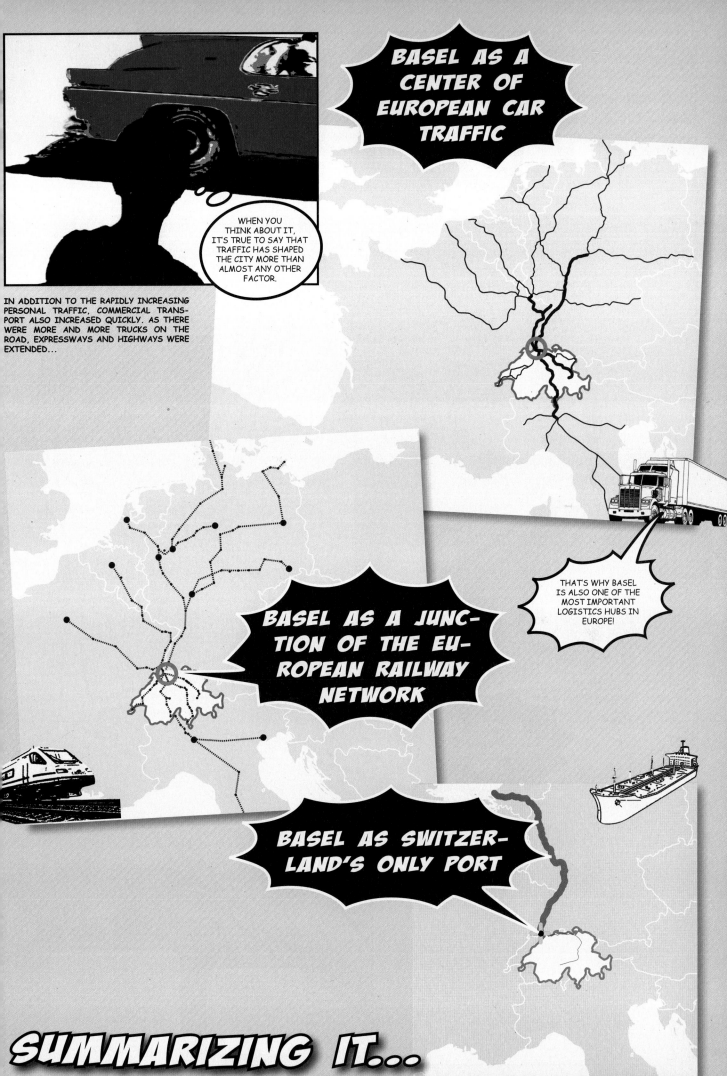

BASEL AS A CENTER OF EUROPEAN CAR TRAFFIC

WHEN YOU THINK ABOUT IT, IT'S TRUE TO SAY THAT TRAFFIC HAS SHAPED THE CITY MORE THAN ALMOST ANY OTHER FACTOR.

IN ADDITION TO THE RAPIDLY INCREASING PERSONAL TRAFFIC, COMMERCIAL TRANSPORT ALSO INCREASED QUICKLY. AS THERE WERE MORE AND MORE TRUCKS ON THE ROAD, EXPRESSWAYS AND HIGHWAYS WERE EXTENDED...

THAT'S WHY BASEL IS ALSO ONE OF THE MOST IMPORTANT LOGISTICS HUBS IN EUROPE!

BASEL AS A JUNCTION OF THE EUROPEAN RAILWAY NETWORK

BASEL AS SWITZERLAND'S ONLY PORT

SUMMARIZING IT...

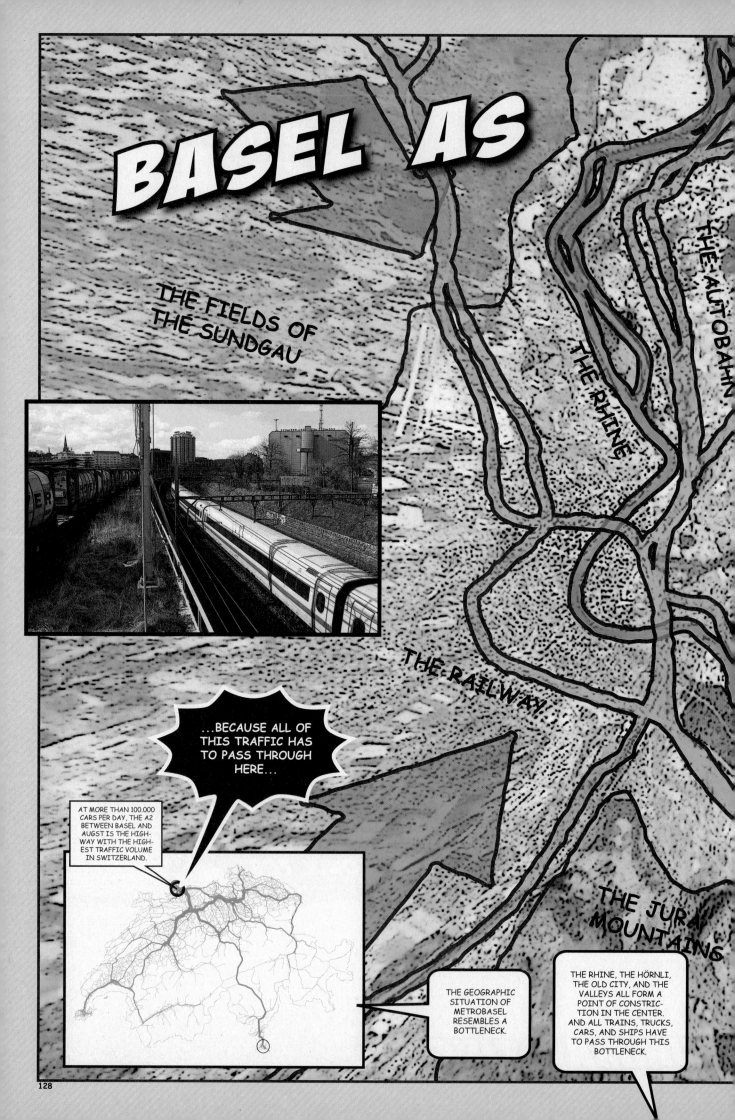

BASEL AS

THE FIELDS OF THE SUNDGAU

THE AUTOBAHN

THE RHINE

THE RAILWAY

...BECAUSE ALL OF THIS TRAFFIC HAS TO PASS THROUGH HERE...

AT MORE THAN 100,000 CARS PER DAY, THE A2 BETWEEN BASEL AND AUGST IS THE HIGHEST-TRAFFIC VOLUME IN SWITZERLAND.

THE JURA MOUNTAINS

THE GEOGRAPHIC SITUATION OF METROBASEL RESEMBLES A BOTTLENECK.

THE RHINE, THE HÖRNLI, THE OLD CITY, AND THE VALLEYS ALL FORM A POINT OF CONSTRICTION IN THE CENTER, AND ALL TRAINS, TRUCKS, CARS, AND SHIPS HAVE TO PASS THROUGH THIS BOTTLENECK.

TRAFFIC AREAS

...AFFIC AREAS REQUIRE MANY BRIDGES AND TUNNELS; BUT APART FROM USUALLY BEING UGLY, THEY ALSO
...SSECT PARTS OF THE CITY, CUTTING THEM OFF FROM ONE ANOTHER.

FINALLY, I'M OUT
OF THAT TUNNEL...

...MODES OF TRANSPORT NOT ONLY CONNECT ☐ THEY ALSO DIVIDE.

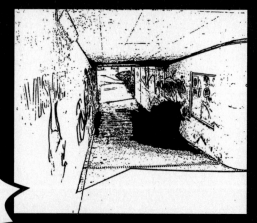

... WELL, THAT
WASN'T A VERY
NICE RIDE ...

AS BLOCKADES

THE NEW CITY WALLS
HOW AM I SUP-POSED TO REACH THE OTHER SIDE???
ON THE ONE HAND, THE REGION BENEFITS TREMEN-DOUSLY FROM ITS FAVORABLE STRATEGIC SITUATION....
AS WE HAVE SEEN, METROBA-SEL IS TRAVERSED BY A NUMBER OF TRAFFIC ROUTES.

LET'S SEE. I'VE GOT THIS ONE IDEA...

LET'S WEAVE THE CITY TOGETHER...

URBAN DIVISION → URBAN STITCHING

MODEL CONCEPT

WEAVING THE CITY TOGETHER

WEAVING TOGEHER

OLYMPIC SCULPTURE PARK, SEATTLE

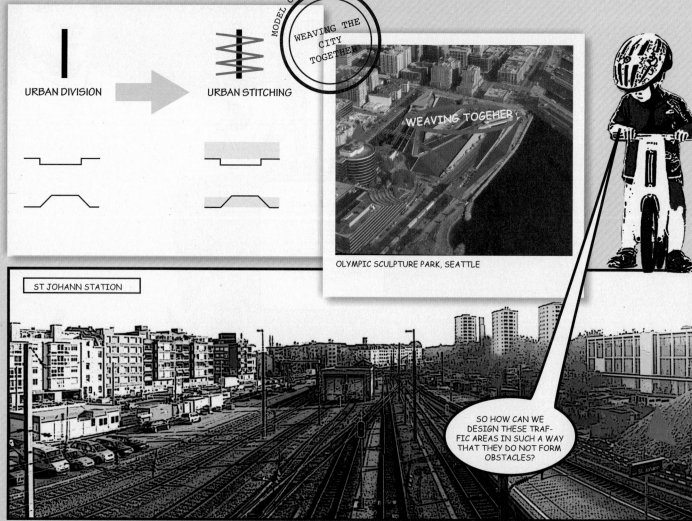

ST JOHANN STATION

SO HOW CAN WE DESIGN THESE TRAFFIC AREAS IN SUCH A WAY THAT THEY DO NOT FORM OBSTACLES?

...WITH NEW PARKS AND BUILDINGS

135

WEAVING THE CITY TOGETHER...

THESE SUGGESTIONS SHOW THAT INFRASTRUCTURE LINES CURRENTLY CUTTING ACROSS THE CITY COULD ALSO BECOME A GREAT POTENTIAL FOR THE CITY, PROVIDING NEW SPACE FOR PARKS, APARTMENTS AND OFFICES, PUBLIC INSTITUTIONS, AND RECREATION AREAS.

BIRSFELDEN

④

SUPERSTRUCTURE

HARDWALD

BEFORE

HERE ARE SOME EXAMPLES OF HOW WE COULD TRANSFORM THE EXISTING OBSTACLES AND BARRIERS OF INFRASTRUCTURE INTO CONNECTING ELEMENTS...

FOR EXAMPLE, A GREEN BRIDGE LINKING BIRSFELDEN WITH HIRZBRUNNEN AND THE HÖRNLI THAT ALSO CREATES SPACE FOR NEW RESIDENTIAL BUILDINGS.

KLEINHÜNINGEN

⑤

WEIL AM RHEIN

BEFORE

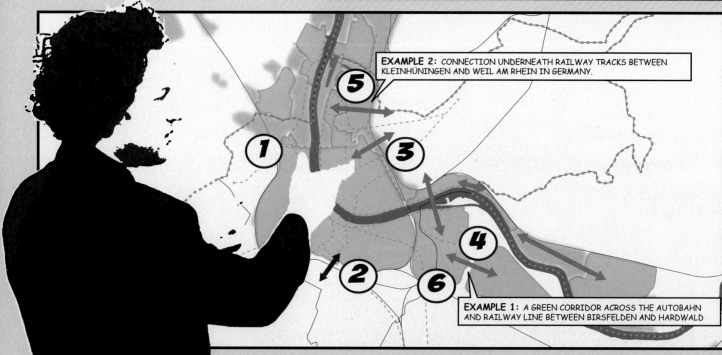

EXAMPLE 2: CONNECTION UNDERNEATH RAILWAY TRACKS BETWEEN KLEINHÜNINGEN AND WEIL AM RHEIN IN GERMANY.

① ⑤ ③ ④ ② ⑥

EXAMPLE 1: A GREEN CORRIDOR ACROSS THE AUTOBAHN AND RAILWAY LINE BETWEEN BIRSFELDEN AND HARDWALD

...WITH GREEN CORRIDORS

EXAMPLE 1: GREEN CORRIDOR ACROSS THE HIGHWAY AND RAILWAY LINE BETWEEN BIRSFELDEN AND HARDWALD

EXAMPLE 2: CONNECTION UNDERNEATH RAILWAY TRACKS BETWEEN KLEINHÜNINGEN AND WEIL AM RHEIN IN GERMANY

BEFORE

AFTER

A NEW RECREATION AND RESIDENTIAL AREA ABOVE THE A2 BETWEEN BIRSFELDEN AND HARDWALD

SHOPPING IN METRO BASEL

> TRADE HAS ALWAYS HAD A SIGNIFICANT INFLUENCE ON THE SHAPE OF CITIES. METROBASEL IS AN EXAMPLE OF HOW COMMERCIAL SPACES CONTINUE TO FORM THE REGION.

GEE IS A STUDENT OF ARCHITECTURE WHO HAS DONE RESEARCH ON SHOPPING AT HARVARD AND ETH STUDIO BASEL.

1

LOCATION:	CITY CENTER
SHOPPING VENUES:	MARKET, DEPARTMENT STORES, CHAIN STORES, SPECIALIZED SHOPS
PRODUCTS:	CLOTHES, BOOKS, JEWELRY, ETC.; GROCERIES
ACCESS:	
PEDESTRIAN	[X]
BICYCLE	[X]
TRAM/BUS	[X]
S-BAHN	[X]
CAR	[ ]

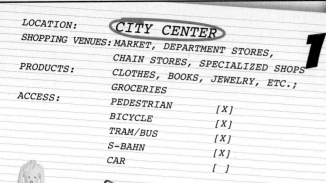

2

LOCATION:	SUBCENTERS
SHOPPING VENUES:	MARKET, DEPARTMENT STORES, CHAIN STORES, SPECIALIZED SHOPS
PRODUCTS:	CLOTHES, BOOKS, JEWELRY, ETC.; GROCERIES
ACCESS:	
PEDESTRIAN	[X]
BICYCLE	[X]
TRAM/BUS	[X]
S-BAHN	[X]
CAR	[ ]

SHOPPING TYPOLOGIES IN THE REGION

Map labels: LÖRRACH, WEIL-AM-RHEIN, HUNINGUE, ST LOUIS, BURGFELDEN, ALLSCHWIL, BINNINGEN, BOTTMINGEN, OBERWIL, LEYMEN, MÜNCHENSTEIN, REINACH, BASEL, MUTTENZ, PRATTELN, LIESTAL

3

LOCATION:	TOWN AND VILLAGE NEIGHBORHOODS
SHOPPING VENUES:	LOCAL STORES
PRODUCTS:	GROCERIES
ACCESS:	
PEDESTRIAN	[X]
BICYCLE	[X]
TRAM/BUS	[X]
S-BAHN	[ ]
CAR	[ ]

GUNDELDINGEN QUARTIER   GUNDELDINGEN QUARTIER   ST JOHANN QUARTIER

4

LOCATION:	OUTSIDE OF TOWN
SHOPPING VENUES:	SHOPPING CENTERS
	CHAIN STORES
PRODUCTS:	GROCERIES, CLOTHES, FURNITURE, GARDENING AND DIY SUPPLIES
ACCESS:	
PEDESTRIAN	[ ]
BICYCLE	[/] VERY DIFFICULT
TRAM/BUS	[/] DIFFICULT
S-BAHN	[ ]
CAR	[X]

AT ETH STUDIO BASEL, GEE EXPLAINS THAT MEDIEVAL BASEL WAS A FREE CITY THAT WAS NOT REQUIRED TO PAY TAXES TO THE EMPEROR. THIS HAD FAVORABLE ECONOMIC EFFECTS. THE GUILDS COULD REGULATE THEIR CRAFTS AND TRADE AUTONOMOUSLY AND INFLUENCED THE DEVELOPMENT OF THE CITY AS AN IMPORTANT COMMERCIAL LOCATION. GOODS WERE PRODUCED IN THE GUILDHALLS, SUCH AS THE SAFRANHAUS, AND SOLD IN MARKET STALLS. THE INFLUENCE OF THE GUILDS BROUGHT WITH IT A SPATIAL RELOCATION OF MUNICIPAL POWER FROM MÜNSTER SQUARE (THE SEAT OF THE BISHOP) TO THE BOURGEOIS MARKETPLACE.

THE CENTER OF THE CITY SHIFTS FROM THE MÜNSTER TO THE MARKET

IN THE MIDDLE AGES, THE BISHOP'S INFLUENCE OVER THE CITY DWINDLED. A CIVIL SOCIETY OF MERCHANTS EMERGED THAT ALSO GAINED POLITICAL INFLUENCE. ITS SPATIAL EMBODIMENT IS THE CONSTRUCTION OF THE CITY HALL BY THE MARKETPLACE. POLITICS WAS NO LONGER THE PREROGATIVE OF THE MÜNSTER ON THE HILL, BUT A MATTER FOR THE MERCHANTS IN THE CITY BELOW.

HAUSGENOSSEN
SCHLÜSSEL
BROTBECKEN
FISCHER
METZGER
SAFFRAN
SCHMIEDE
SCHNEIDER
SCHUMACHER
REBLEUTE
WEBER

FISCHMARKT
MITTLERE BRÜCKE
RHEIN
MARKETPLACE
MÜNSTER SQUARE
SPALENBERG
FREIESTRASSE
BARFÜSSERPLATZ
STEINENVORSTADT

THE GUILDS SHAPED THE CITY

THE MARKETPLACE IN ITS PRESENT SIZE AND SHAPE IS THE WORK OF LATE 19TH CENTURY URBAN CONSTRUCTION. BEFORE THEN, ITS NORTHERN HALF FEATURED A QUADRANGLE OF HOUSES THAT OBSCURED THE CHANCELLERY WING OF THE CITY HALL FROM VIEW. THE CORN MARKET, AS IT WAS CALLED THEN, DIPPED DOWNWARDS FROM EAST TO WEST AND OPENED UP TOWARDS SATTELGASSE ONTO A SMALL SQUARE WITH A FOUNTAIN.

FROM: 'BASEL ARCHITECTURE GUIDE', P. 215

1661

PROSPECT DES KORNMARCKTS ZU BASEL.

MARKETPLACE, 1881

BEFORE REMODELLING

AFTER REMODEL-

THE MARKET AS A MEDIEVAL COMMERCIAL CENTER

CONSTRUCTION OF NORTHERN PART

NO TOWER YET ON THE CITY HALL!

MARKETPLACE

1881 — BEFORE REMODELLING

1905 — AFTER REMODELLING

WE SEE THAT THE MODERN-DAY MARKET SQUARE IS ONLY 100 YEARS OLD. EVEN THE TOWER ON THE CITY HALL IS ALMOST NEW. AND WE CALL IT THE 'OLD CITY'!

DEPARTMENT STORES

THE LATE 19TH AND EARLY 20TH CENTURY WAS A TIME OF INDUSTRIALIZATION, MODERNIZATION, AND GROWTH IN THE CITY OF BASEL. DURING THESE YEARS, MANY NEW CONSTRUCTION TYPES WERE DEVELOPED THAT ARE STILL AROUND TODAY. FOR EXAMPLE, **THE DEPARTMENT STORE.**

THE PUBLIC SPACE BECOMES A PLACE OF LEISURE! IN LATE 19TH-CENTURY EUROPE, THE FIGURE OF THE 'FLANEUR' EMERGED:* A CITY DWELLER WHO ENJOYS STROLLING THROUGH THE STREETS AND OBSERVING CITY LIFE AS WELL AS GOODS ON SALE.

*THE 'FLANEUR' WAS PORTRAYED BY FRENCH AUTHOR BAUDELAIRE AND LATER INTRODUCED INTO ACADEMIC THEORY BY WALTER BENJAMIN

ADVERTISEMENT, 'BASLER NACHRICHTEN', AROUND 1900

EMERGENCE OF MODERN BOURGEOIS SOCIETY

AROUND 1900, THE FIRST DEPARTMENT STORES WERE BUILT IN BASEL. THIS NEW TYPE OF COMMERICAL VENUE COVERED A LARGE SALES AREA THAT USUALLY EXTENDED OVER SEVERAL FLOORS. A SINGLE STORE OFFERED A WIDE RANGE OF GOODS: A NEW TYPOLOGY OF BUILDING HAD BEEN DEVELOPED. ANOTHER NOTABLE ASPECT WAS THAT PRICES WERE NO LONGER NEGOTIABLE. IN THE FIRST DECADES, THESE STORES AIMED AT ATTRACTING CUSTOMERS WITH DEEP POCKETS. GOODS WERE OFTEN ELABORATELY ARRANGED AND WERE NOT ONLY AVAILABLE TO BUY, BUT ALSO PRESENTED FOR VIEWING WITHOUT AN OBLIGATION TO PURCHASE. THIS CREATED A WHOLE NEW ATMOSPHERE, TRANSFORMING SHOPPING INTO A LEISURE ACTIVITY.

FREIE STRASSE

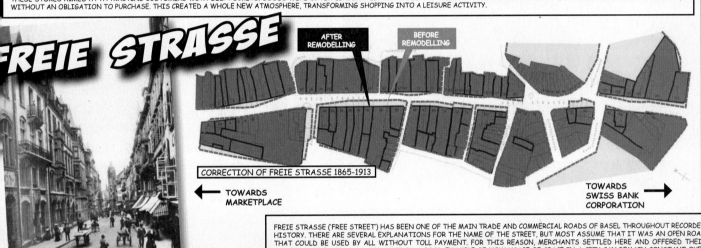

AFTER REMODELLING

BEFORE REMODELLING

CORRECTION OF FREIE STRASSE 1865-1913

← TOWARDS MARKETPLACE

TOWARDS SWISS BANK CORPORATION →

FREIE STRASSE, 1890

FREIE STRASSE ('FREE STREET') HAS BEEN ONE OF THE MAIN TRADE AND COMMERCIAL ROADS OF BASEL THROUGHOUT RECORDED HISTORY. THERE ARE SEVERAL EXPLANATIONS FOR THE NAME OF THE STREET, BUT MOST ASSUME THAT IT WAS AN OPEN ROAD THAT COULD BE USED BY ALL WITHOUT TOLL PAYMENT. FOR THIS REASON, MERCHANTS SETTLED HERE AND OFFERED THEIR WARES, AS THEY STILL DO TODAY. IT IS A GOOD EXAMPLE OF HOW USAGE OF SPACE IN A CITY CAN REMAIN CONSTANT OVER CENTURIES WITHOUT CHANGING, EVEN AS THE OLDER BUILDINGS ARE REPLACED BY NEWER ONES. THE FUNCTIONAL ZONES OF A CITY ARE FREQUENTLY LONGER-LASTING THAN THE ACTUAL BUILDINGS.

THE ECONOMIC BOOM AT THE TURN FROM THE 19TH TO THE 20TH CENTURY KICKED OFF THE INTENSIVE CONSTRUCTION ACTIVITY. THE OLD MEDIEVAL BUILDINGS WERE REGARDED AS UNECONOMICAL, IMPRACTICAL, AND OLD-FASHIONED. PEOPLE LOOKED CONFIDENTLY TO THE FUTURE AND WANTED NEW STRUCTURES. A GREAT NUMBER OF NEW TRADE AND COMMERCIAL BUILDINGS WERE CONSTRUCTED. TODAY WE REGARD THESE BUILDINGS AS HISTORIC AND PRESERVE THEM, ALTHOUGH THEY ARE RELATIVELY NEW AND OLDER BUILDINGS WERE TORN DOWN TO MAKE PLACE FOR THEM. ANOTHER EXAMPLE OF A CITY IN CONSTANT CHANGE.

Baumleingasse 16

Eisengasse 11 b.1839

Eisengasse 12 b.1909

Eisengasse 14 b.1907

Freiestrasse 2 b.1907

Freiestrasse 4 b.1908

Freiestrasse 8

Freiestrasse 9 b.1901

Freiestrasse 11 b.1902

Freiestrasse 23 b.1906

Freiestrasse 26 b.1900

MOST OF THE BUILDINGS HERE LOOK OLD, BUT AREN'T REALLY. HARDLY ANY OF THEM ARE OLDER THAN 100 YEARS.

Freiestrasse 28 b.1898

Freiestrasse 36 b.1906

Freiestrasse 42 b.1895

Freiestrasse 43 b.1910

Freiestrasse 44 b.1896

MICHEL DECIDES TO WALK DOWN FREIE STRASSE ONE MORE TIME. AT THE VERY LEAST, THEY HAVE TO FIND A NICE DRESS FOR PATRICIA...

MICHEL WONDERS WHETHER BASEL'S CONSERVATISM MIGHT BE LINKED TO THE CITY'S RELIGIOUS BACKGROUND. BASEL IS STRONGLY INFLUENCED BY A LEGACY OF PROTESTANT-ISM. THE 'PROTESTANT ETHIC' DESCRIBED BY MAX WEBER IS DISTINGUISHED BY MOD-ERATION AND INDUSTRIOUSNESS AND REGARDS PROFESSIONAL SUCCESS AS AN IDEAL TO BE ACHIEVED. IT GOES HAND IN HAND WITH FRUGALITY THAT DISDAINS GLAMOUR AND EXTERNAL BEAUTY.

* MAX WEBER (1864-1920), THE FOUNDER OF MODERN SOCIOLOGY. HIS MAIN WORK, 'THE PROTESTANT ETHIC AND THE SPIRIT OF CAPITALISM', WAS PUBLISHED IN 1904. IT IS A STUDY OF THE RELATION-SHIP BETWEEN ECONOMICS AND RELIGION.

BASICALLY, WE CAN DISTINGUISH FOUR DIFFERENT PLACES AND MODES OF SHOPPING. EACH TYPE GIVES RISE TO DIFFERENT URBAN SPACES AND VARIETIES OF ARCHITECTURE. WE WILL LOOK AT THESE MATTERS SYSTEMATICALLY...

WE HAVE ALREADY SEEN SOME OF THE CITY CENTER. LET ME GIVE YOU ANOTHER COMPARATIVE OVERVIEW AND TELL YOU A LITTLE ABOUT ACCESSIBILITY.

SHOPPING TYPE 1: IN THE CITY CENTER

ALTHOUGH IT IS SUCH AN EVERYDAY MATTER, THE EFFECTS ON THE CITY ARE NOT SO EASY TO DESCRIBE.

SINCE THE MIDDLE AGES, THE CITY CENTER HAS BEEN THE MAIN PLACE FOR TRADE AND SHOPPING, WHERE THE GREATEST RANGE OF GOODS CAN BE FOUND.

GERMANY

FRANCE

SWITZERLAND

LOCATION: CITY CENTER **1**
SHOPPING VENUES: MARKET, DEPARTMENT STORES, CHAIN STORES, SPECIALIZED SHOPS
PRODUCTS: CLOTHES, BOOKS, JEWELRY, ETC.; GROCERIES
ACCESS:

PEDESTRIAN	[X]
BICYCLE	[X]
TRAM/BUS	[X]
S-BAHN	[X]
CAR	[ ]

THE OLD CITY AS SHOPPING CENTER*

CLARAPLATZ

MITTLERE BRÜCKE

MARKETPLACE

RHINE

FREIE STRASSE

SPALENBERG

WETTSTEINBRÜCKE

STEINENVORSTADT

FREIE STRASSE

MANOR
MIGROS
Jelmoli HOLDING AG
GLOBUS SAVOIR VIVRE
coop city

*OF COURSE THE OLD CITY IS NOT A SHOPPING CENTER, BUT THE TWO SHARE SOME IMPORTANT ASPECTS. LET'S TAKE THIS THOUGHT ONE STEP FURTHER AND IMAGINE THE RANGE OF SHOPS BEING 'CURATED', AS IN A SHOPPING MALL. THEN WE CAN ASK OURSELVES: 'WHICH FUNCTIONS ARE MISSING IN THE CITY CENTER?'

FELDBERGSTRASSE

IMAGINE A CITY CENTER FEATURING BOTH HIGH-END SHOPS AND AREAS WHERE INTERESTING YOUNG DESIGNERS CAN OPEN SHOPS AT AFFORDABLE RATES; PLACES TO ENJOY, TO RELAX IN, WHERE YOU CAN SEE INTERESTING THINGS AND WHERE SHOPPING CAN TURN INTO A REAL EXPERIENCE... ESSENTIALLY, THIS MEANS 'CURATING' THE CITY CENTER.

MODEL CITY CENTER

W HOTEL, NEW YORK

BOUTIQUE HOTEL

THERME, VALS

SPA

MODEL CONCEPT

INNER CITY SHOPPING TYPOLOGIES

...THIS WAY, THE VARIETY OF OPTIONS IN THE CITY CENTER COULD BE SHAPED PURPOSEFULLY AND WITH A BROADER RANGE.

GREEN SPACES ALONG THE RHINE

SPA ALONG THE RHINE

YOUNG DESIGNERS

BOUTIQUE HOTELS

HIGH-END BOUTIQUE

GLOBAL HIGH-END BRANDS

PARK LEADING TO THE RHINE

HMMM... HOW BEAUTIFUL! A HOTEL AND SPA IN THE MIDDLE OF THE CITY CENTER.

'CURATING'* SHOPPING ZONES

ZAGATSURVEY.
2007 BASEL RESTAURANTS

CRITERIA FOR A GOOD CITY CENTER

[✓] Excellent museums
[✓] Excellent restaurants
[✓] Great Shopping
[✓] Hotels und Wellness
[✓] Green spaces and public areas

*'CURATING' IS A TERM FROM THE ART WORLD REFERRING TO THE SELECTION, CARE, AND ORGANIZATION OF AN EXHIBITION OR ART COLLECTION (FROM LATIN CURA, 'CARE'). IN THE CONTEXT OF SHOPPING, IT REFERS TO THE ASSEMBLY AND ORGANIZATION OF DIFFERENT SHOPPING ZONES.

TOD'S
MARC JACOBS
GUCCI
PRADA
FENDI Dior
MARNI

AOOH! THE NEW
B A R N E Y S
N E W Y O R K
IN BASEL

MODEL CONCEPT

CITY SHOPPING TYPES

DIOR,
LUXURY SHOPPING DISTRICT
AOYAMA, TOKYO

GLOBAL HIGH-END

FEMME
HOMME
CHAUSSURES

*BARNEYS IS AN EXCLUSIVE US DEPART-
MENT STORE CARRYING INNOVATIVE AND
CONTEMPORARY FASHION BRANDS SUCH
AS MARC JACOBS, MANOLO BLAHNIK, OR
HELMUT LANG. IN A WAY, IT THUS ALSO
PROMOTES THE CREATION OF YOUNG
FASHION. THERE ARE NO DEPARTMENT
STORES LIKE THAT IN BASEL.

BASEL HIGH-END

HEY BASEL.
HERE I COME!

HMMM... I
WONDER WHETHER
SARAH JESSICA
PARKER IS ALSO A
PROTESTANT?

SARAH JESSICA PARKER ('SEX AND THE
CITY') IS NOTORIOUS FOR HER SHOPPING
SPREES AND IS A REGULAR CUSTOMER AT
BARNEYS NEW YORK.

FRENCH CHEESE!

CRÈMERIE FROMAGERIE

IN THE OLD CITIES AND VILLAGES SURROUNDING BASEL, MICHEL AND PATRICIA WANT TO EXPERIENCE THE SPECIAL QUALITIES OF THE REGION...

HMMM... EVERY TIME YOU CROSS THE FRENCH BORDER, YOU CAN SENSE A VERY SPECIFIC LOCAL TOUCH, ALTHOUGH YOU'RE ONLY A FEW HUNDRED METERS AWAY FROM BASEL.

NEIGHBORHOOD STORES IN THE SUBCENTERS OF METROBASEL ARE ALSO PART OF THE THIRD CATEGORY OF SHOPPING. OFTEN, THEY ARE HOME TO VERY SPECIFIC LOCAL PRODUCTS OR TRADITIONS.

BOULANGERIE!!

Wir arbeiten ohne Gentechnik!

ORGANIC FARMS RUN BY LOCAL FARMERS.

TWO KILOS OF NON-GM APPLES, PLEASE!

LOSS OF DISTINCTIVENESS

GUESS WHO'S FROM GERMANY, HEE HEE

IN THE SUNDGAU REGION, NORTHWEST OF BASEL, MOST OF THE SHOPS ARE SLOWLY DISAPPEARING:

THIS MAP SHOWS HOW DIFFICULT IT IS FOR SMALLER BUSINESSES TO COMPETE WITH LARGE DEPARTMENT STORES. IN THE SUNDGAU, LOCAL SUPPLY OF BASIC COMMODITIES HAS ALL BUT DISAPPEARED!

THERE ARE HARDLY ANY BOULANGERIES (BAKERIES), BOUCHERIES (BUTCHERS), EPICERIES (GROCERS) OR RESTAURANTS IN THE VILLAGES OF THE SUNDGAU. THIS RESULTS IN A LOSS OF LOCAL CHARACTER AND DISTINCTIVENESS.

>10

5-10

2-5

1

BOULANGER

BOUCHERIE

L'EPICERIE

RESTAURANT

SHOPPING OPTIONS IN THE RURAL AREAS ARE DWINDLING!

METROBASEL MAP

THIS DISPLACEMENT OF LOCAL CHARACTER COINCIDES WITH A PROCESS OF SUBURBANIZATION: THERE IS A DANGER OF VILLAGES TURNING INTO FACELESS SUBURBS.

COMPETITION WITH HYPERMARCHÉS

SHOPPING TYPE 3: NEIGHBORHOOD SHOPS

THE THIRD IMPORTANT TYPOLOGY OF SHOPPING IN THE REGION IS THE CITY QUARTER WITH SUPERMARKETS AND 'ECKLÄDELI' (CORNER SHOPS). THEIR RANGE OF PRODUCTS USUALLY COVERS EVERYDAY NECESSITIES.

TWO CORPORATIONS, COOP AND MIGROS, ARE PARTICULARLY ACTIVE HERE. THEY WERE FOUNDED AT THE BEGINNING OF THE 20TH CENTURY.

EASY ACCESSIBIL-ITY AND THE HIGH DENSITY OF SMALL GROCERY STORES ARE HALLMARKS OF URBAN QUALITY OF LIFE IN SWITZERLAND. LARGE SHOPS ARE MORE OF AN EXCEPTION.

⬤ MIGROS-COOP CLUSTER

• CORNER SHOP

WE SHOULD HURRY UP AND TRY TO GET THE REST OF OUR GROCERIES BEFORE THE SHOPS CLOSE...

BUT WE CAN STILL BUY SOMETHING LATER IF WE STOP BY THE 'ECKLÄDELI'.

ONE OF THE FIRST MOBILE MIGROS SHOPS IN 1925

MIGRO/COOP VS ECKLÄDELI

FAMILY STORES, OFTE[N] CALLED ECKLÄDELI, AR[E] ALLOWED TO DO BUSI-NESS IN THE EVENING[S] AND ON SUNDAYS IN[ ] BASEL. THEY ARE OFTE[N] OWNED BY NON-SWIS[S] FAMILIES AND OFFER T[HE] CHANCE OF STARTING A[N] INDEPENDENT BUSINES[S]

LOCATION: TOWN AND VILLAGE NEIGHBORHOODS **3**

SHOPPING VENUES: LOCAL STORES

PRODUCTS: GROCERIES

ACCESS:
- PEDESTRIAN [X]
- BICYCLE [X]
- TRAM/BUS [X]
- S-BAHN [ ]
- CAR [ ]

GUNDELDINGEN QUARTER

GUNDELDINGEN QUARTER

ST. JOHANN QUARTER

OPENING HOURS
SUPERMARKET
MO-FR 09:00-18:30
SAT 09:00-17:00
SUN **CLOSED**

OPENING HOURS
ECKLÄDELI
MO-FR 07:00-22:00
SAT 07:00-22:00
SUN 07:00-22:00

MIGROS, MÜLHAUSERSTRASSE

ECKLÄDLI, MÜLHAUSERSTRASSE

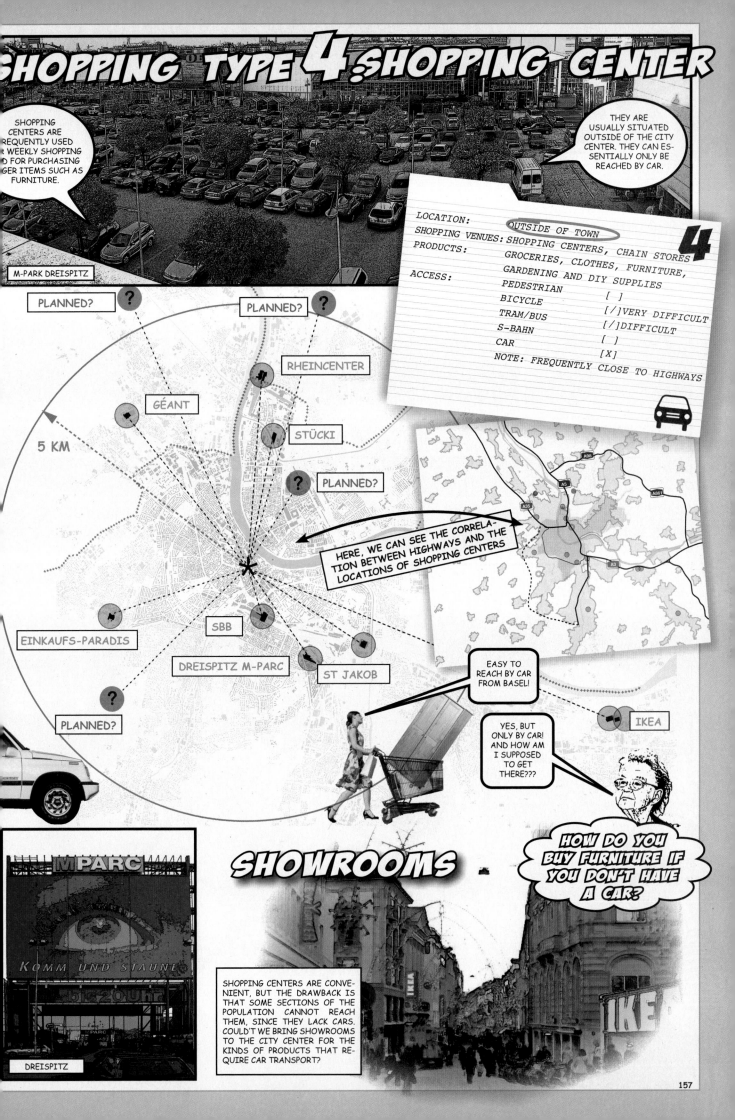

SHOPPING CENTERS ARE FREQUENTLY USED FOR WEEKLY SHOPPING AND FOR PURCHASING LARGER ITEMS SUCH AS FURNITURE.

M-PARK DREISPITZ

THEY ARE USUALLY SITUATED OUTSIDE OF THE CITY CENTER. THEY CAN ESSENTIALLY ONLY BE REACHED BY CAR.

LOCATION: OUTSIDE OF TOWN
SHOPPING VENUES: SHOPPING CENTERS, CHAIN STORES
PRODUCTS: GROCERIES, CLOTHES, FURNITURE, GARDENING AND DIY SUPPLIES
ACCESS:
PEDESTRIAN [ ]
BICYCLE [/]VERY DIFFICULT
TRAM/BUS [/]DIFFICULT
S-BAHN [ ]
CAR [X]
NOTE: FREQUENTLY CLOSE TO HIGHWAYS

PLANNED?

PLANNED?

RHEINCENTER

GÉANT

STÜCKI

5 KM

PLANNED?

HERE, WE CAN SEE THE CORRELATION BETWEEN HIGHWAYS AND THE LOCATIONS OF SHOPPING CENTERS

EINKAUFS-PARADIS

SBB

DREISPITZ M-PARC

ST JAKOB

PLANNED?

EASY TO REACH BY CAR FROM BASEL!

YES, BUT ONLY BY CAR! AND HOW AM I SUPPOSED TO GET THERE???

IKEA

SHOWROOMS

HOW DO YOU BUY FURNITURE IF YOU DON'T HAVE A CAR?

KOMM UND STAUNE

SHOPPING CENTERS ARE CONVENIENT, BUT THE DRAWBACK IS THAT SOME SECTIONS OF THE POPULATION CANNOT REACH THEM, SINCE THEY LACK CARS. COULD'T WE BRING SHOWROOMS TO THE CITY CENTER FOR THE KINDS OF PRODUCTS THAT REQUIRE CAR TRANSPORT?

DREISPITZ

MICHEL AND PATRICIA ARE TOURING THE NEARBY SHOPPING CENTERS, SINCE THEY STILL NEED A FEW THINGS FOR THE PARTY THAT EVENING...

ST LOUIS, FRANCE

PRATTELN, SWITZERLAND

SHOPPING CENTERS ARE BOTH POPULAR AND DETESTED BECAUSE THEY OFFER CHEAP GOODS, A LARGE SELECTION, AND PARKING SPACES NEARBY.

WEIL-AM-RHEIN, GERMANY

HOW DOES THE CITY CENTER COMPARE TO THE SHOPPING CENTER?

PUBLIC TRANS-PORT

CITY CENTER

SHOPPING CENTERS CAN BE THE SIZE OF A CITY CENTER...

...OR SOMETIMES EVEN BIGGER!!!

PRIVATE TRANSPORT

SHOPPING CENTER

West Edmonton Mall
1985
Edmonton, Alberta
Maurice Sunderland
apotheosis of the cluster

THE CITY CENTER OF BASEL HAS ONLY 400.000 M2 OF BUILDING AREA. BUT EDMONTON MALL HAS 570.000 M2!

159

STÜCKI

THE NEW 'STÜCKI' SHOPPING CENTER IS A GOOD EXAMPLE FOR BASEL (AND THE WHOLE OF SWITZERLAND, TOO). IT WILL BE NOTABLE FOR EXTREMELY HIGH-CLASS SHOPPING OPPORTUNITIES AND A GOOD QUALITY OF ARCHITECTURE AND URBAN DESIGN.

IT IS VERY EASY TO REACH BY PUBLIC TRANSPORT AND IS ALSO CONVENIENTLY CLOSE TO THE GERMAN AND FRENCH PARTS OF METROBASEL.

I WONDER WHETHER I CAN BUY MY HELMUT LANG DRESS HERE?

METROBASEL HIGHEND

DESIGNED BY ARCHITECTS DIENER AND DIENER, THE STÜCKI CENTER WILL OPEN IN 2009.

AFTER A LONG DRIVE THROUGH THE REGION, THEY RETURN TO BASEL IN THE AFTERNOON AND TRY TO GET A HOLD OF SOME DELICACIES AT THE MARKET. BUT...

HMM... THE TOMATOES DON'T LOOK SO GREAT THOUGH...

LET'S SEE IF I CAN FIND THE LAST INGREDIENTS HERE...

WHERE CAN I FIND GOOD INGREDIENTS AROUND HERE??

T THEY SEEM TO BE QUITE PUT OFF BY THE GOODS, ESPECIALLY BY WAY THEY ARE PRESENTED.

LOOK, THERE'S JAY.* HE CAN'T FIND ANY SATISFACTORY PRODUCTS HERE EITHER.

SOMEHOW, ALL OF THIS COULD BE PRESENTED MUCH MORE APPEAL-INGLY.

YOU'D EXPECT A LITTLE MORE FROM A MARKET IN A REGION LIKE THIS...

MARKETPLACE

MODEL CONCEPT

LOCAL DELICACIES

Y OWNS A GREAT IN-AN RESTAURANT IN ST HANNS-VORSTADT.

FINE FOODS FRESH MARKETS SPECIALTIES

WINE TASTING WITH LOCAL VINTNERS

EVENT

FRESHLY PREPARED FOOD AND FINE FOOD COOKING EVENTS

FRESH FLOWERS LIKE IN THE MARCHÉ DES ENFANTS ROUGES, PARIS

SPECIALTY FRESH MARKET

A MODEL CITY CENTER

IMAGINE A COMPLETELY DIFFERENT KIND OF MARKET WHERE YOU CAN SHOP, EAT, DRINK, AND TALK IN AN EXCITING ABMIANCE. SUCH MARKETS ARE FOUND IN MANY CITIES, SUCH AS PARIS, LONDON, OR TORONTO.

SHOPPING:

WE IMAGINE A REGION WHERE THE **STRENGTHS AND DISTINCTIVE FEATURES** OF THE INDIVIDUAL PARTS ARE FOSTERED. **REGIONAL CENTERS** SUCH AS LÖRRACH, ST LOUIS, OR RHEINFELDEN SHOULD DEVELOP THEIR SOMETIMES CENTURIES-OLD **TRADITION AS TRADING TOWNS**. PRODUCTS SUCH AS BADEN WINE FROM THE MARKGRÄFLERLAND OR JURA CHEESE ARE EVIDENCE OF A REGIONAL WAY OF LIFE AND CULINARY CULTURE. **THIS CULTURE SHOULD BE STRENGTHENED.**

THE CITY CENTER OF BASEL IS THE **FOCAL POINT OF REGIONAL TRADE**. THE GOOD CONNECTION TO THE OTHER CITIES OF THE REGION PROVIDED BY THE **'HERZSTÜCK' URBAN RAILWAY** (PAGE 125) IS SO IMPORTANT BECAUSE IT ALLOWS EASY ACCESS TO THE CITY CENTER FOR THE ENTIRE POPULATION OF METROBASEL. THE **URBAN CATCHMENT AREA WITH A POPULATION OF OVER 800.000** WOULD ALLOW A MUCH **GREATER RANGE OF GOODS** TO BE OFFERED THAN IS CURRENTLY THE CASE. IN THE CITY CENTER, THE **HIGH-END** AND THE MORE AFFORDABLE, **INNOVATIVE MARKET SEGMENTS** NEED TO BE COVERED BETTER. WE ALSO ENVISAGE THE **MARKET BEING TURNED INTO A SHOPPING EXPERIENCE** MODELLED ON THE EXAMPLES OF LONDON OR PARIS.

SHOPPING CENTERS AS PLACES OF PURCHASE ARE FREQUENTLY CONTROVERSIAL. WE SUGGEST RECONCEPTUALIZING THESE SHOPPING CENTERS: **AS PLACES WHERE PEOPLE FROM THE REGION GET TOGETHER AND MEET**. THEY SHOULD BE PLACES WHERE **VENDORS OF SPECIALTIES** CAN OFFER THEIR GOODS TO A BROADER RANGE OF CUSTOMERS. SHOPPING CENTERS SHOULD BE **DESIGNED TO BE MUCH MORE APPEALING** AND SHOULD BE EFFICIENTLY **LINKED TO PUBLIC TRANSPORT**. WE VIEW THE STÜCKI ESTATE AS A GOOD EXAMPLE.

BIO IST DIE ZUNKUNFT!!

LEARNING IN METRO BASEL

CITIES ARE PLACES OF LIFELONG LEARNING THAT TAKES PLACE IN SCHOOLS, RESEARCH INSTITUTES, UNIVERSITIES, ART INSTITUTES, AND IN CHURCHES AND OTHER RELIGIOUS INSTITUTIONS...

CLAUDIA STUDIES ARCHITECTURE AT ETH STUDIO BASEL

ON SATURDAY MORNING, MICHEL VISITS THE VITRA DESIGN MUSEUM IN WEIL AM RHEIN. HE IS REALLY IMPRESSED WITH THE BUILDING BY FRANK GEHRY AND THE INTERESTING EXHIBITION. NOW HE IS LOOKING FORWARD TO HIS BRUNCH DATE WITH PATRICIA AT THE KUNSTMUSEUM.

OH, IT WOULD BE GREAT TO SHOW UP FOR MY DATE WITH PATRICIA IN A SMART, FAST CAR. BUT I OUGHT TO BE ABLE TO CATCH A BUS HERE TOO.

...THE VITRA DESIGN MUSEUM, NORTH OF BASEL IN WEIL AM RHEIN..

MEANWHILE, PATRICIA IS AT THE SCHAULAGER WITH MANY OTHER PEOPLE VISITING THE LATEST EXHIBITION. SHE REMEMBERS HER DATE WITH MICHEL AND RUNS OUT TO CATCH THE TRAM...

...THE SCHAULAGER AT THE SOUTHERN EDGE OF THE CITY IN A COMMERCIAL PARK...

167

THE KUNSTMUSEUM IN THE CITY CENTER

THE MUSEUM HAS A TERRIFIC COLLECTION. BUT WHY ISN'T MICHEL HERE YET?

MEANWHILE, IN THE KUNSTMUSEUM...

PATRICIA IS A LITTLE UNEASY, BUT MAYBE THAT'S ONLY BECAUSE A GROUP OF NOISY CHILDREN JUST WALKED INTO THE ROOM.

AAAW, I DON'T WANT TO WAIT THAT LONG. THAT'S CRAZY!! WHY DON'T YOU WALK TO RIEHEN AND I'LL MEET YOU AT THE 'BEYELER'.

PATRICIA'S MO-BILE PHONE

MICHEL CALLS TO SAY THAT THE BUS ONLY RUNS ONCE EVERY HOUR, AND JUST BARELY MISSED THE LAST ONE!

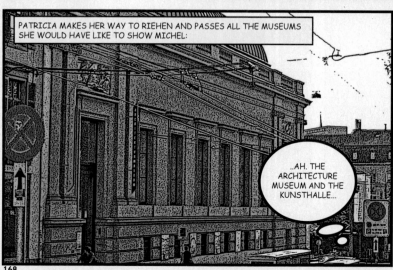

PATRICIA MAKES HER WAY TO RIEHEN AND PASSES ALL THE MUSEUMS SHE WOULD HAVE LIKE TO SHOW MICHEL:

..AH. THE ARCHITECTURE MUSEUM AND THE KUNSTHALLE...

THE HISTORY MUSEUM

*THE HISTORY MUSEUM IS IN THE BARFÜSS-ER CHURCH, THE FORMER MONASTERY OF A MENDICANT ORDER. IT IS NOT THE FIRST TIME THE CHURCH WAS CONVERTED FOR OTHER PURPOSES: IN THE 19TH CENTURY, IT SERVED AS A STORAGE DEPOT!

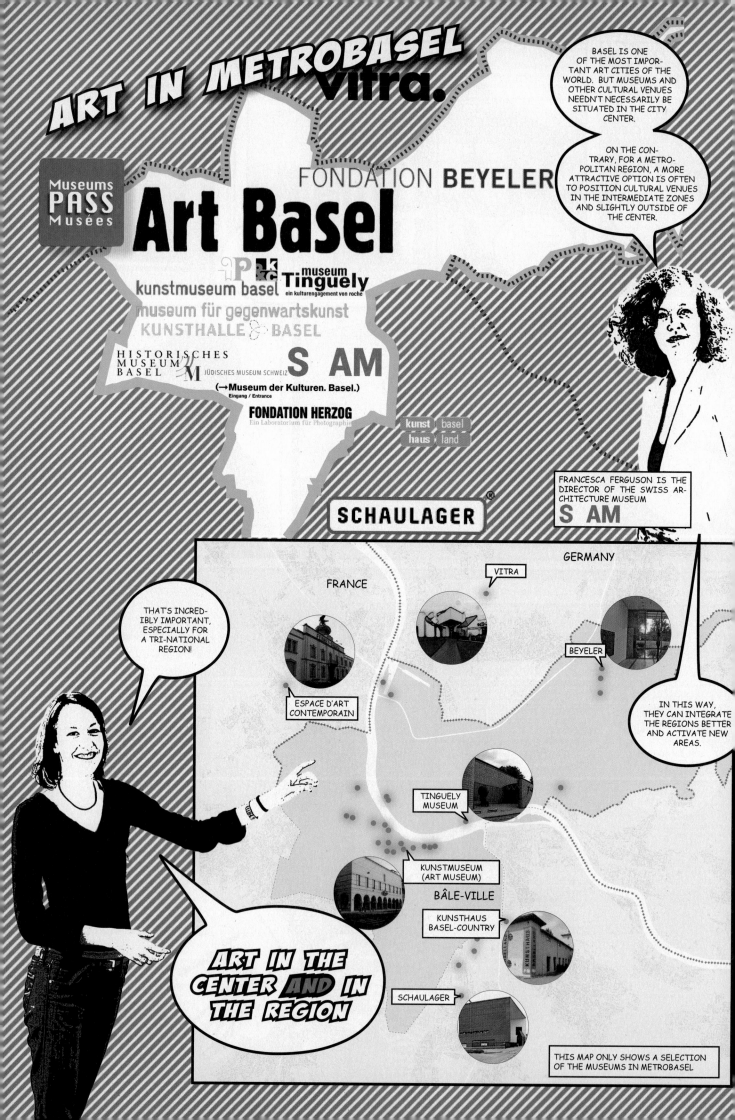

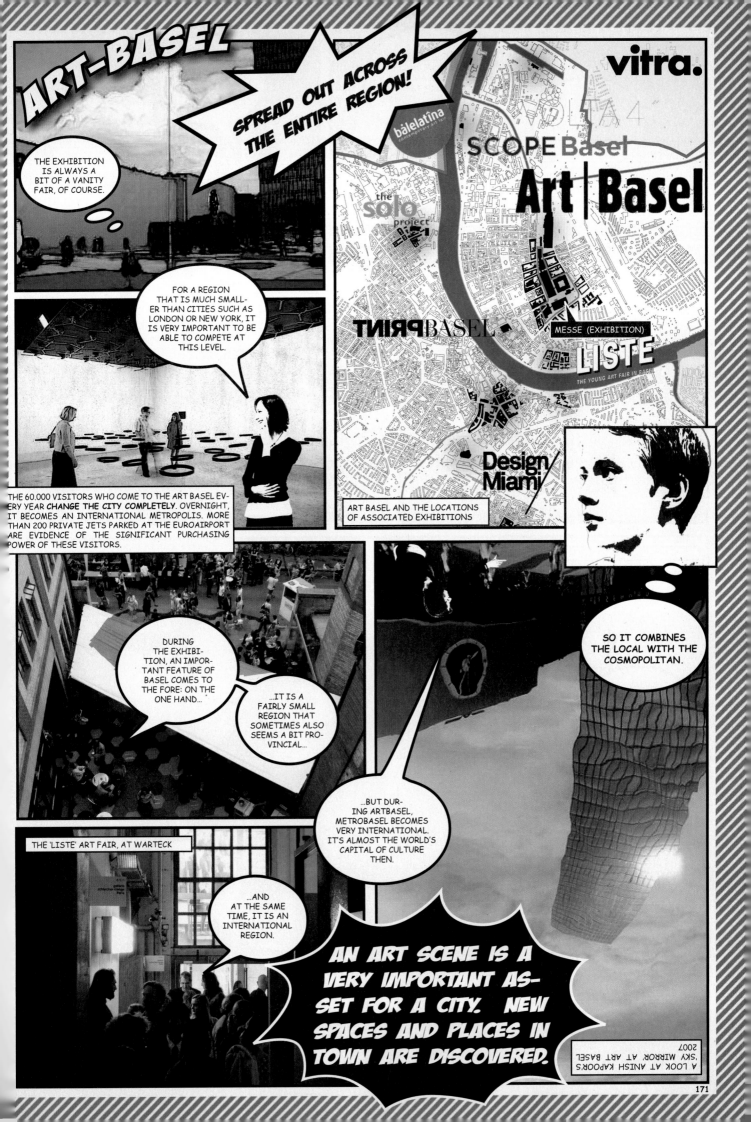

MUSEUM OF CONTEMPORARY ART

KUNSTHALLE, BASEL

ESPACE D'ART CONTEMPORAIN, ST LOUIS, FRANCE

SPACE FOR CONTEMPORARY ART IN THE PERIPHERY

SOMEHOW THE NATIONAL BOUNDARIES SEEM TO PREVENT THE EMERGENCE OF SUCH VENUES OCCUPIED BY ARTISTS ELSEWHERE.

DO YOU REMEMBER THOSE COOL ART STUDIOS IN THE BROOKLYN DOCKYARDS?

EVEN STUTTGART HAS THE NORD-BAHNHOF, WHICH IS HOME TO MANY ARTISTS.

ART STUDIO AND EXHIBITION SPACE, WILLIAMSBURG, NEW YORK

OFTEN, THE HINTERLAND OF A CITY HAS MORE SPACE AND AFFORDABLE LOCATIONS, PROVIDING MORE ROOM FOR ART AND CULTURE.

REUSE

P.S 1

EXHIBITION SPACE

STUDIO SPACE

PERIPHERY

MODEL CONCEPT

CONTEMPORARY ART

P.S. 1 CONTEMPORARY ART CENTER, QUEENS, NYC

EVENTS!!

5 POINTZ, ART STUDIOS OPPOSITE PS1

EXEMPLARY LOCATIONS OF CONTEMPORARY ART

AND ART PRODUCTION

......PLACES WHERE WORLD-CLASS CONTEMPORARY ART IS CREATED AND EXHIBITED. FOR A CITY THAT SETS GREAT STORE BY ART, THIS IS VERY IMPORTANT.

'WARM-UP' WEEKEND SUMMER PARTIES

'WARM-UP' WEEKEND SUMMER PARTIES

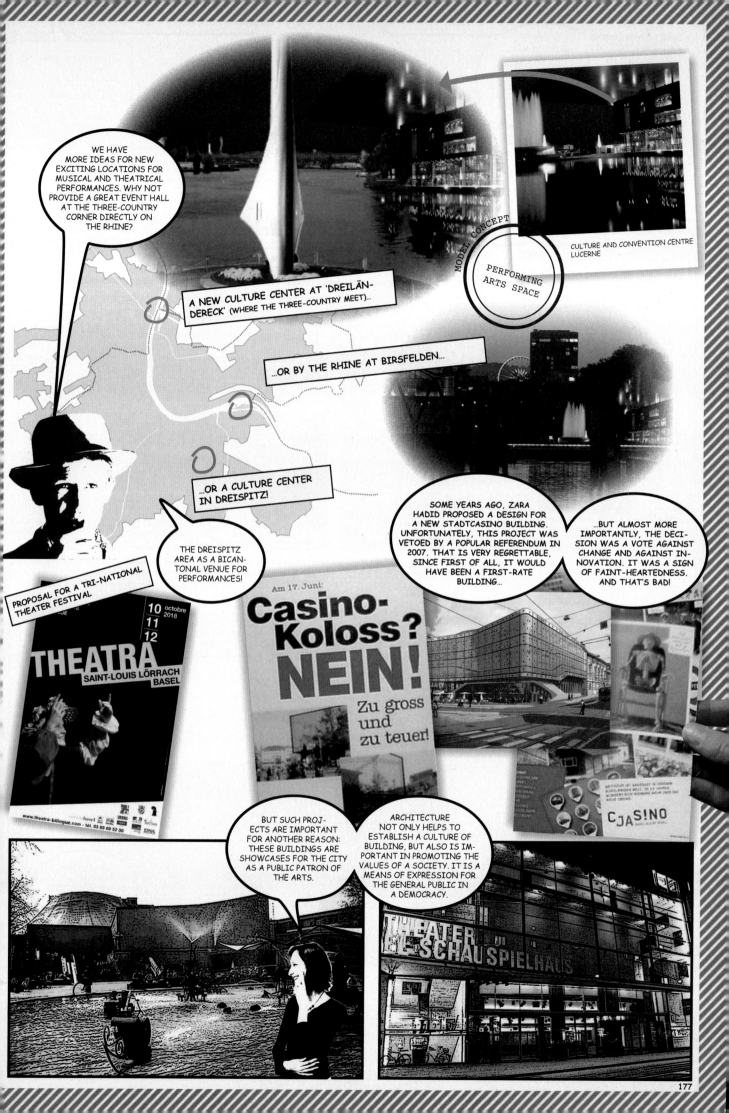

177

BESIDES MUSEUMS AND THEATERS, OTHER PROJECTS ARE IMPORTANT IN REPRESENTING THE CITY OR THE STATE AS PATRONS FOR LEARNING AND WHICH ARE IMPORTANT FOR URBAN DEVELOPMENT...

...CONSTRUCTION OF SCHOOLS, FOR EXAMPLE, HAS LONG BEEN A TASK FOR PUBLIC AUTHORITES. IN BASEL, SUCH BUILDINGS ARE OF A HIGH ARCHITECTURAL QUALITY.

THE BUILDING ON THE KOHLENBERG IS AT THE SAME HEIGHT AS THE BASEL MÜNSTER. ITS CONSTRUCTION REPRESENTS, AT THE TIME, THE ESTABLISHMENT OF SECULAR EDUCATION INDEPENDENT OF THE ECCLESIASTICAL INSTITUTIONS.

DREIROSEN SCHOOL, ADDITIONBUILT BY MORGER DEGELO ARCHITECTS IN 1996

THE LEONHARD HIGH SCHOOL IS IN THE CITY CENTER IN A QUITE DISTINCTIVE BUILDING, CONSTRUCTED IN 1884.

TRADITION OF SCHOOL BUILDINGS IN BASEL

VOLTA SCHOOL, MILLER & MARANTA ARCHITECTS, 2000

VOGESEN SCHOOL, DIENER & DIENER ARCHITECTS, 1996

THE SECONDARY SCHOOL AT AESCH (1959-1962) WAS DESIGNED BY WALTER FÖRDERER IN COLLABORATION WITH R. OTTO AND H. ZWIMPFER. IT IS CONSIDERED ONE OF THE BEST EXAMPLES OF PUBLIC CONSTRUCTION OF ITS TIME. THE SCULPTURAL QUALITY OF THE ROUGH CONCRETE CONTRASTS WITH SKYLIGHTS AND AIRY SPACES IN THE INTERIOR, ESPECIALLY IN THE FOYER.

THE SECONDARY SCHOOL AT AESCH, SOUTH OF BASEL, IS CERTAINLY ONE OF SWITZERLAND'S MOST BEAUTIFUL AND ARCHITECURALLY INTERESTING SCHOOLHOUSES!

MY MOTHER SAID SCHOOL BUILDINGS WERE 'MOTORS' OF ARCHITECTURE!!

SECONDARY SCHOOL, AESCH

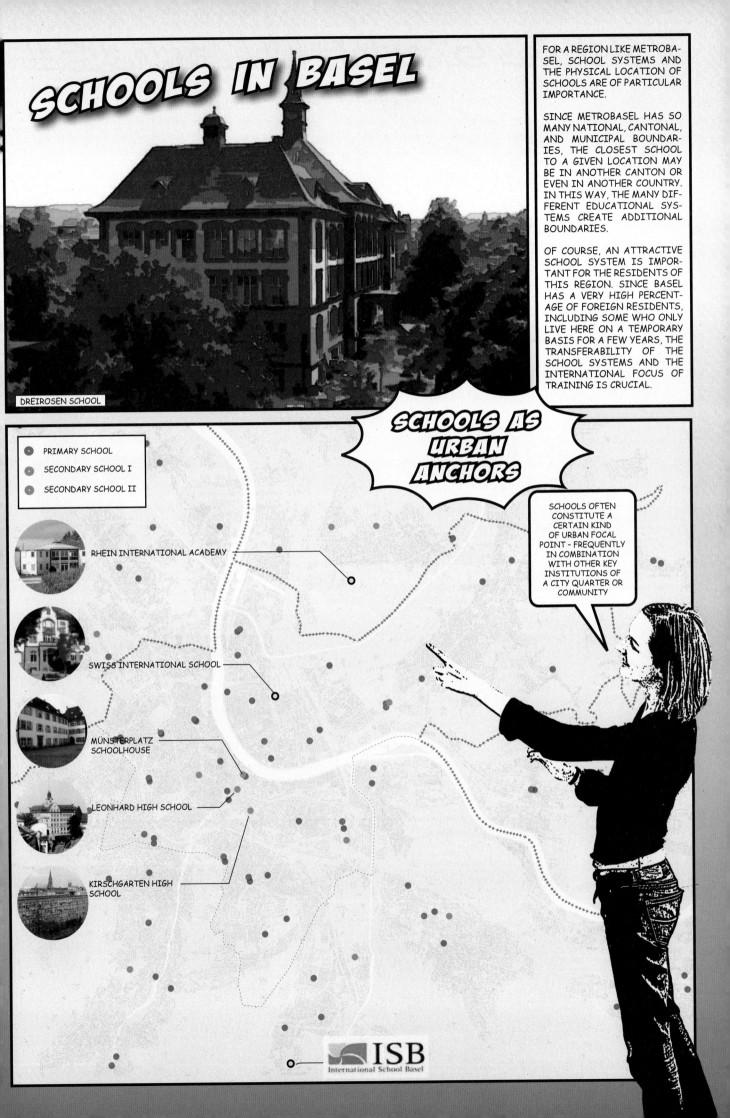

SCHOOLS IN BASEL

DREIROSEN SCHOOL

FOR A REGION LIKE METROBASEL, SCHOOL SYSTEMS AND THE PHYSICAL LOCATION OF SCHOOLS ARE OF PARTICULAR IMPORTANCE.

SINCE METROBASEL HAS SO MANY NATIONAL, CANTONAL, AND MUNICIPAL BOUNDARIES, THE CLOSEST SCHOOL TO A GIVEN LOCATION MAY BE IN ANOTHER CANTON OR EVEN IN ANOTHER COUNTRY. IN THIS WAY, THE MANY DIFFERENT EDUCATIONAL SYSTEMS CREATE ADDITIONAL BOUNDARIES.

OF COURSE, AN ATTRACTIVE SCHOOL SYSTEM IS IMPORTANT FOR THE RESIDENTS OF THIS REGION. SINCE BASEL HAS A VERY HIGH PERCENTAGE OF FOREIGN RESIDENTS, INCLUDING SOME WHO ONLY LIVE HERE ON A TEMPORARY BASIS FOR A FEW YEARS, THE TRANSFERABILITY OF THE SCHOOL SYSTEMS AND THE INTERNATIONAL FOCUS OF TRAINING IS CRUCIAL.

SCHOOLS AS URBAN ANCHORS

SCHOOLS OFTEN CONSTITUTE A CERTAIN KIND OF URBAN FOCAL POINT - FREQUENTLY IN COMBINATION WITH OTHER KEY INSTITUTIONS OF A CITY QUARTER OR COMMUNITY

PRIMARY SCHOOL

SECONDARY SCHOOL I

SECONDARY SCHOOL II

RHEIN INTERNATIONAL ACADEMY

SWISS INTERNATIONAL SCHOOL

MÜNSTERPLATZ SCHOOLHOUSE

LEONHARD HIGH SCHOOL

KIRSCHGARTEN HIGH SCHOOL

ISB
International School Basel

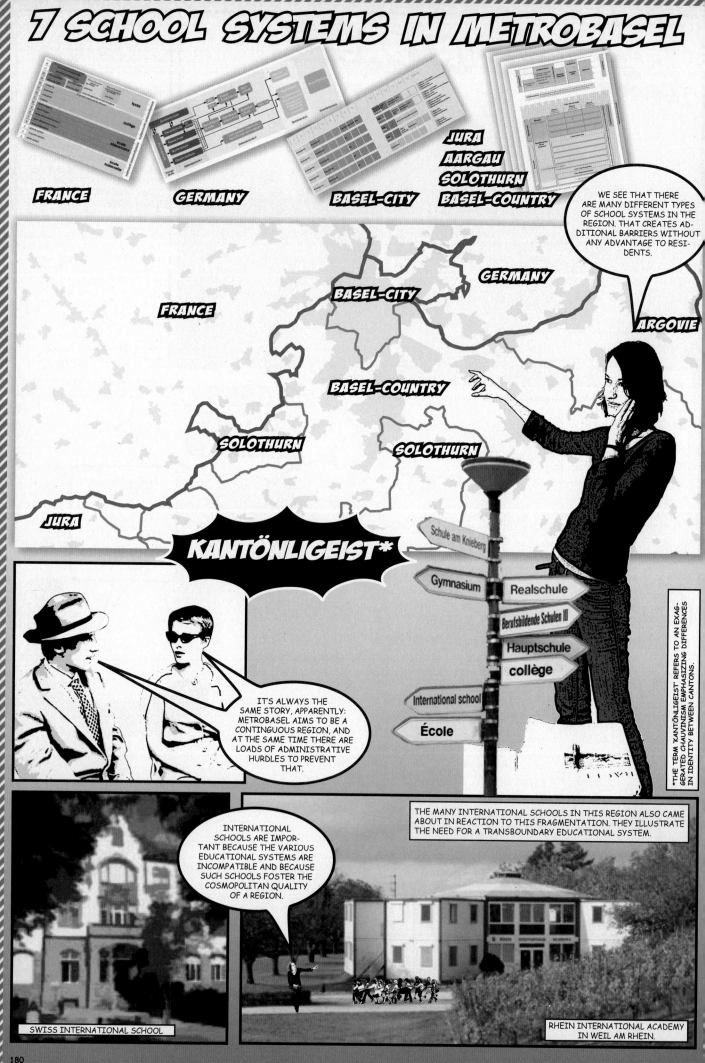

WE MOVED HERE BECAUSE IT'S CLOSE TO THE SCHOOL!

RESIDENTIAL AREAS OFTEN EMERGE IN THE NEIGHBORHOOD OF SCHOOLS

INTERNATIONAL SCHOOL BASEL

...AND NEW RESIDENTIAL AREAS USUALLY REQUIRE NEW SCHOOLS.

I AM A NEW SCHOOL IN A NEWLY DEVELOPED RESIDENTIAL AREA!

SCHOOL BUILDINGS ARE 'ACTORS' IN URBAN DEVELOPMENT. THEY CAN BE 'ATTRACTORS'. FAMILIES MOVE TO PARTS OF TOWN OFFERING BETTER SCHOOLS. QUARTERS WITH POOR SCHOOLS ARE AVOIDED. AND NEW QUARTERS NEED NEW SCHOOLS.

CLAUDIA DEMONSTRATES THAT WHILE NEW SCHOOLS ARE BEING BUILT IN THE NEWLY DEVELOPED ESTATES OUTSIDE THE CITY CENTER, SCHOOLS IN THE CENTER OFTEN LACK STUDENTS. THIS IS BECAUSE OF THE QUALITY OF LIVING IN THE CITY CENTER.

OH MAN. THERE SHE GOES AGAIN. SHE'S ALWAYS RAISING HER HAND, THAT LITTLE MISS KNOW-IT-ALL.

I KNOW THE ANSWER! PLEASE, PLEASE CALL ON ME!!!

WEEEELL, MY DEAR CHILDREN, TODAY, WE'LL DISCUSS THE TOPIC OF 'LEARNING'.

SO, WHAT DO YOU KNOW ABOUT LEARNING IN A CITY?

PSST, ACHIM. I GOT THE NEW X-BOX. IT'S AWESOME!!

COOL! I'LL COME OVER LATER.

DECREASING NUMBER OF STUDENTS!

CLASS SIZE IN BASEL-CITY

DECREASING NUMBER OF STUDENTS

SCHOOLS CLOSED TO MAINTAIN CLASS SIZES

2000 2001 2002 2003 2004 2005 2006

Klassen (linke Skala) · Schüler (linke Skala) — Klassengrösse (rechte Skala)

THE SCHOOLS IN THE CITY CENTER ARE GOOD, BUT IF THERE WERE BETTER APARTMENTS, WE'D HAVE MORE STUDENTS TO FILL THOSE SCHOOLS.

NEW APARTMENTS!!

MORE APARTMENTS FOR THE SCHOOLS IN THE CENTER

THE CITY MUST REMAIN ATTRACTIVE AS A PLACE TO LIVE IN ORDER TO ENSURE A SUFFICIENT POPULATION FOR MAINTAINING SCHOOLS AND CULTURAL VENUES.

183

IN FRONT OF THE MAIN UNIVERSITY BUILDING

UNIVERSITY OF BASEL - THE OLDEST IN SWITZERLAND...

HA! THE UNIVERSITY OF ZURICH WAS NOT FOUNDED UNTIL 1833. BUT WE'RE NOT TRYING TO COMPETE.

THE UNIVERSITY IS CLOSELY RELATED TO THE PRINTING INDUSTRY. THE UNIVERSITY NEEDED PRINTERS TO REPRODUCE THE WRITINGS OF ITS SCHOLARS. IN TURN, THE SKILLFUL PRINTERS ATTRACTED FAMOUS SCHOLARS TO THE CITY.

THIS ILLUSTRATION SHOWS THE SOLEMN FOUNDATION OF THE UNIVERSITY IN 1460. IT WAS FOUNDED BY POPE PIUS II, THE FORMER CLERK OF THE COUNCIL OF BASEL. HUMANISTS LIKE ERASMUS OF ROTTERDAM MOVED TO BASEL. THE PRINTING PRESS WAS INTRODUCED. PARACELSUS AND HOLBEIN LIVED IN THE CITY.

THE PRINTING INDUSTRY

THE FIRST UNIVERSITY IN SWITZERLAND!

MANY SMART PEOPLE CAME TO WORK IN BASEL BECAUSE OF ITS UNIVERSITY. CENTERS OF LEARNING HAVE LONG BEEN RECOGNIZED AS IMPORTANT FACTORS OF URBAN DEVELOPMENT.

THE OLDEST REMAINING MAIN BUIILDING OF THE UNIVERSITY IS ON THE RHINE.

PROF. DR. ANTONIO LOPRIENO, RECTOR OF THE UNIVERSITY OF BASEL

BOLOGNA, FOUNDED IN 1088, IS CONSIDERED THE OLDEST UNIVERSITY IN THE WORLD.

THE UNIVERSITY OF VIENNA, FOUNDED IN 1365, IS THE OLDEST UNIVERSTIY IN THE GERMAN-SPEAKING WORLD.

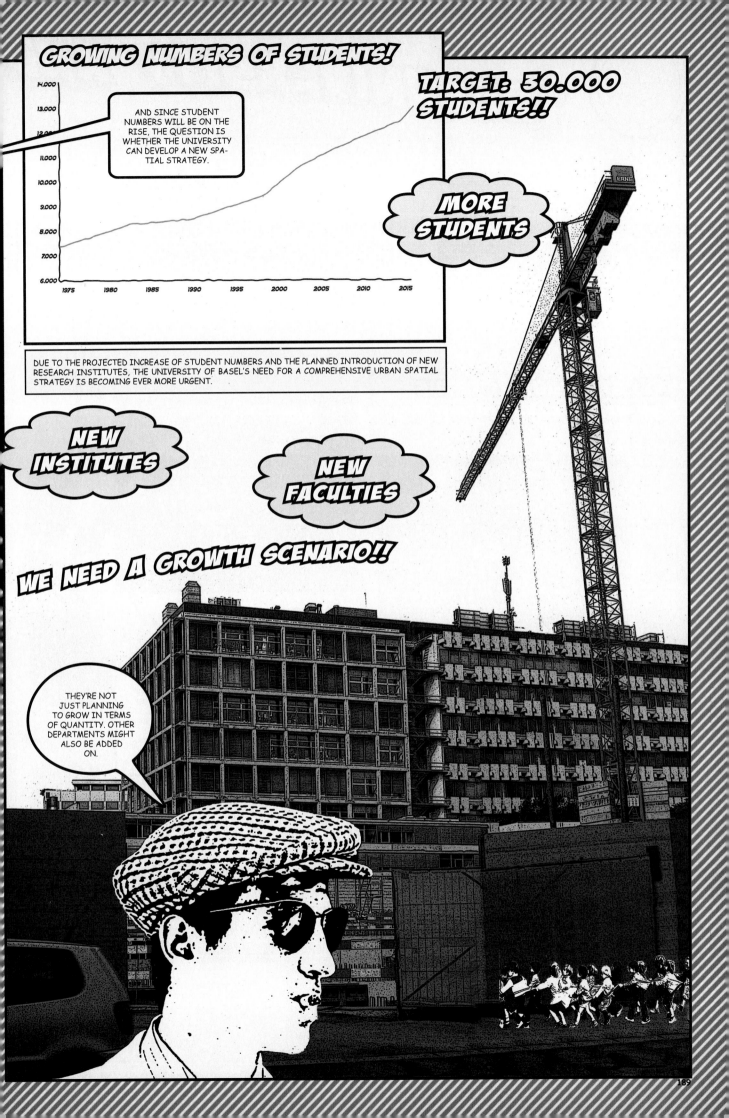

THE UNIVERSITY AND

EPFL, LAUSANNE

UNIVERSITY OUT-SIDE OF THE CITY

MIT, HARVAR AND BOSTON UNIVERSITY, CAMBRIDGE/ BOSTON, USA

UNIVERSITY ALONG-SIDE A RIVER

WHAT OTHER SPATIAL MODELS ARE THERE FOR A UNIVERSITY WITHIN A CITY? LET'S LOOK AT A FEW EXEMPLARY CITIES:

RELATIONSHIP OF THE UNIVERSITY AND THE CITY

UNIVERSITY OF URBINO

INSTITUTES IN THE CITY

UNIVERSITY OF BASEL

AND IN BASEL?

MODEL CONCEPT

INTERNATIONAL INSTITUTES

AND WHY DON'T WE BRING THE BEST RE-SEARCH INSTITUTES OF THE THREE COUN-TRIES TO METROBA-SEL AND USE THAT AS THE BASIS FOR AN URBAN DEVELOPMENT STRATEGY?

MAX PLANCK INSTITUTE, BERLIN

MAX-PLANCK-GESELLSCHAFT

INSTITUT PASTEUR, PARIS

INSTITUT PASTEUR

RESEARCH INSTITUTES
WE SHOULD MOVE THE PASTEUR AND MAX PLANCK INSTITUTES TO METROBASEL. THEY COULD JOIN WITH THE UNIVERSITY HERE TO FORM A SPATIAL UNITY.
A CHAIN OF KNOWLEDGE REACHING FROM THE CITY CENTER AND THE UNIVERSITY OF BASEL ACROSS THE *CAMPUS PLUS* TO THE RHINE.
INSTITUT PASTEUR
MAX-PLANCK-GESELLSCHAFT
HELMHOLTZ | GEMEINSCHAFT
BASEL NORTH
CAMPUS OF KNOWLEDGE
THIS COULD BE THE END POINT OF THE CHAIN OF KNOWLEDGE AND AT THE SAME TIME ENHANCE THE QUALITY OF THE NEW CITY QUARTER.
AS PART OF THE *CAMPUS PLUS* PROJECT, NEW PLACES OF RESEARCH AND TEACHING FOR SEVERAL THOUSAND STUDENTS AND SCHOLARS WILL BE CREATED BY 2015.
UNIVERSITY OF BASEL
WHAT A BRILLIANT IDEA TO ADVANCE URBAN DEVELOPMENT THROUGH THE INSTITUTES...
FHNW
Basler Zeitung

WHILE RESEARCH AND TEACHING CURRENTLY TAKES PLACE MAINLY IN UNIVERSITIES, SCHOOLS, AND RESEARCH INSTITUTES, CHURCHES AND MONASTERIES USED TO BE IMPORTANT PLACES OF LEARNING ALSO. EVEN TODAY, THEY ARE STILL IMPORTANT FOR CULTURAL LIFE AND OF COURSE ALSO FOR RELIGIOUS LIFE IN THE CITY AND LEAVE A STRONG MARK ON URBAN DEVELOPMENT.

THE CHURCHES AND MONASTERIES OF BASEL ARE JUST AS IMPORTANT FOR THE HISTORY OF THE CITY (AND USED TO ALSO BE PLACES OF LEARNING AND STUDYING)

PREDIGERKIRCHE. FORMERLY THE CHAPEL OF A DOMINICAN MONASTERY, IS NEAR THE DANCE OF DEATH (SEE THE INTRODUCTORY CHAPTER) RIGHT BESIDE THE UNIVERSITY HOSPITAL AND THE UNIVERSITY.

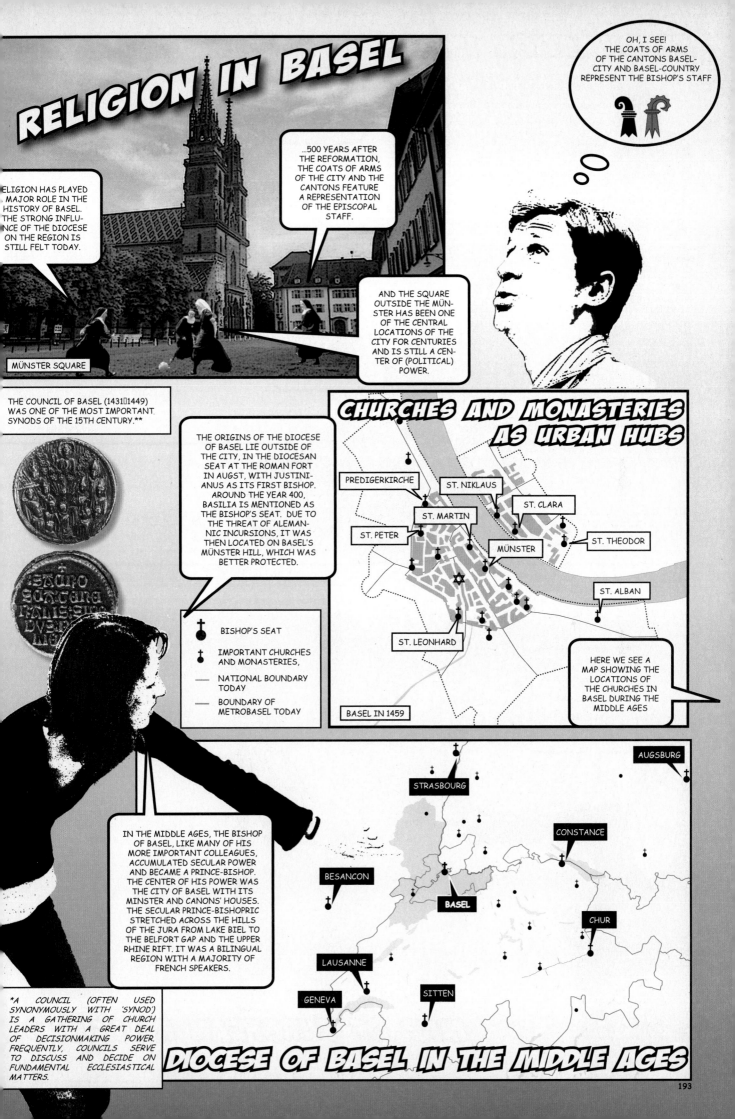

RELIGION IN BASEL

OH, I SEE! THE COATS OF ARMS OF THE CANTONS BASEL-CITY AND BASEL-COUNTRY REPRESENT THE BISHOP'S STAFF

RELIGION HAS PLAYED A MAJOR ROLE IN THE HISTORY OF BASEL. THE STRONG INFLUENCE OF THE DIOCESE ON THE REGION IS STILL FELT TODAY.

...500 YEARS AFTER THE REFORMATION, THE COATS OF ARMS OF THE CITY AND THE CANTONS FEATURE A REPRESENTATION OF THE EPISCOPAL STAFF.

AND THE SQUARE OUTSIDE THE MÜNSTER HAS BEEN ONE OF THE CENTRAL LOCATIONS OF THE CITY FOR CENTURIES AND IS STILL A CENTER OF (POLITICAL) POWER.

MÜNSTER SQUARE

THE COUNCIL OF BASEL (1431–1449) WAS ONE OF THE MOST IMPORTANT SYNODS OF THE 15TH CENTURY.**

THE ORIGINS OF THE DIOCESE OF BASEL LIE OUTSIDE OF THE CITY, IN THE DIOCESAN SEAT AT THE ROMAN FORT IN AUGST, WITH JUSTINIANUS AS ITS FIRST BISHOP. AROUND THE YEAR 400, BASILIA IS MENTIONED AS THE BISHOP'S SEAT. DUE TO THE THREAT OF ALEMANNIC INCURSIONS, IT WAS THEN LOCATED ON BASEL'S MÜNSTER HILL, WHICH WAS BETTER PROTECTED.

CHURCHES AND MONASTERIES AS URBAN HUBS

PREDIGERKIRCHE

ST. NIKLAUS

ST. CLARA

ST. MARTIN

ST. PETER

MÜNSTER

ST. THEODOR

ST. ALBAN

ST. LEONHARD

BASEL IN 1459

✝ BISHOP'S SEAT

✝ IMPORTANT CHURCHES AND MONASTERIES

— NATIONAL BOUNDARY TODAY

— BOUNDARY OF METROBASEL TODAY

HERE WE SEE A MAP SHOWING THE LOCATIONS OF THE CHURCHES IN BASEL DURING THE MIDDLE AGES

IN THE MIDDLE AGES, THE BISHOP OF BASEL, LIKE MANY OF HIS MORE IMPORTANT COLLEAGUES, ACCUMULATED SECULAR POWER AND BECAME A PRINCE-BISHOP. THE CENTER OF HIS POWER WAS THE CITY OF BASEL WITH ITS MINSTER AND CANONS' HOUSES. THE SECULAR PRINCE-BISHOPRIC STRETCHED ACROSS THE HILLS OF THE JURA FROM LAKE BIEL TO THE BELFORT GAP AND THE UPPER RHINE RIFT. IT WAS A BILINGUAL REGION WITH A MAJORITY OF FRENCH SPEAKERS.

*A COUNCIL (OFTEN USED SYNONYMOUSLY WITH 'SYNOD') IS A GATHERING OF CHURCH LEADERS WITH A GREAT DEAL OF DECISIONMAKING POWER. FREQUENTLY, COUNCILS SERVE TO DISCUSS AND DECIDE ON FUNDAMENTAL ECCLESIASTICAL MATTERS.

STRASBOURG

AUGSBURG

CONSTANCE

BESANCON

BASEL

CHUR

LAUSANNE

GENEVA

SITTEN

DIOCESE OF BASEL IN THE MIDDLE AGES

REFORMATION 1529

THE REFORMATION WAS A MOVEMENT OF RENEWAL DURING THE 16TH CENTURY THAT LED TO A SCHISM IN THE CHRISTIAN CHURCH BETWEEN CATHOLIC, LUTHERAN, AND REFORMED CHURCHES. THE REFORMATION IN BASEL IS CLOSELY CONNECTED TO THE REFORMER JOHANNES OEKOLAMPAD. SINCE THE MID-1620S, HE HAD LED THE REFORMED CAMP AND WAS IN REGULAR CONTACT WITH REFORMERS SUCH AS LUTHER OR ULRICH ZWINGLI IN ZURICH.

AS EARLY AS 1528, ORNAMENTS HAD BEEN REMOVED AND STATUES SMASHED IN SEVERAL BASEL CHURCHES. AT THE END OF THE YEAR, THE ATMOSPHERE IN THE CITY WAS APPROACHING CIVIL WAR, WITH CONFLICTS BETWEEN REFORMERS AND TRADITIONAL BELIEVERS. THE FOLLOWING YEAR, THE REFORMATION MANAGED TO ASSERT ITSELF.

J. OEKOLAMPAD (1482-1531)
STATUE IN THE BASEL MÜNSTER

ICONOCLASM IN THE BASEL MÜNSTER: EVEN TODAY, WE CAN STILL SEE THE DAMAGE DONE TO THE CRUCIFIXION GROUP IN 1529.

MARTIN LUTHER (1483-1546) WAS THE THEOLOGICAL INSTIGATOR AND TEACHER OF THE REFORMATION.

THE FIRST BIBLES IN GERMAN ARE PRINTED IN BASEL!

IN 1529, THE BISHOP WAS EXPELLED FROM BASEL AND HAD TO FIND A NEW SEAT.

BETWEEN 1529 AND 1621, PORRENTRUY WAS THE SEAT OF THE BISHOP; FROM 1621-1828 IT WAS IN ARLESHEIM; AND SINCE THEN, THE DIOCESAN SEAT OF BASEL HAS BEEN IN SOLOTHURN.

BASEL

ARLESHEIM

PORRENTRUY

SOLOTHURN

REFORMED
CATHOLIC
ORTHODOX
MUSLIM

BASEL IS SITUATED NEAR ANOTHER BOUNDARY: THE RELIGIOUS BOUNDARY. THIS HAD AN IMMENSE IMPACT OF THE HISTORY OF THE CITY.

BASEL

MAP OF EUROPEAN RELIGIONS

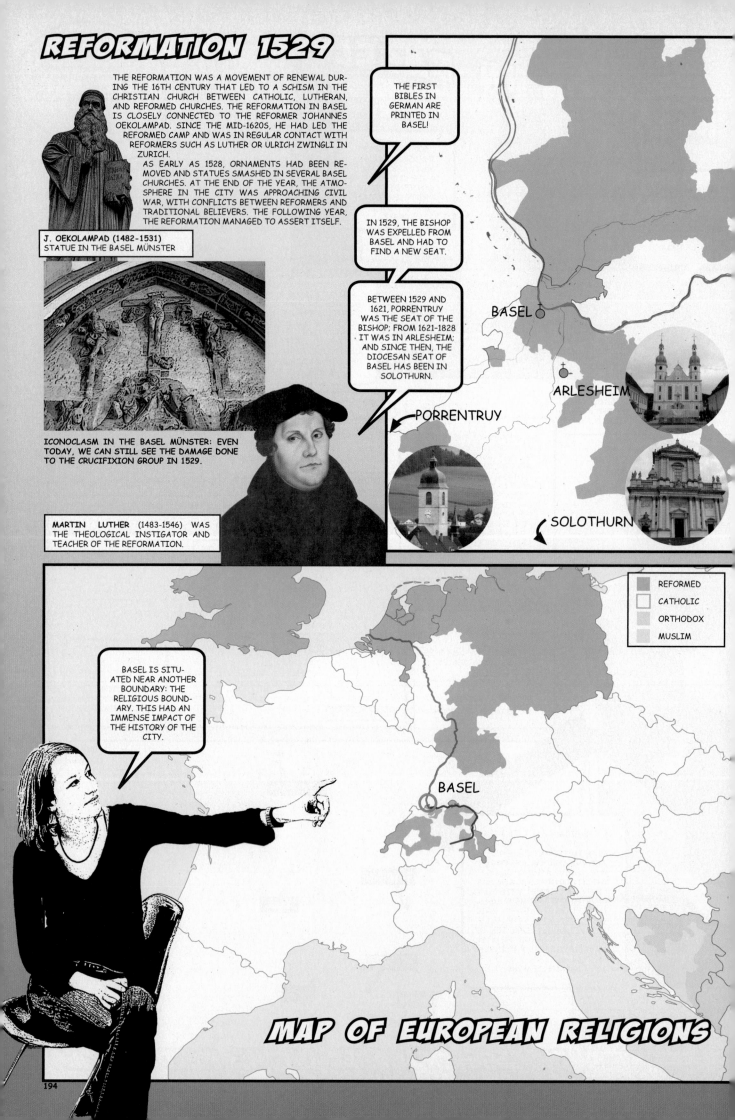

THE EFFECTS OF THE REFORMATION

AFTER THE REFORMATION IN 1529, THE CATHOLIC CHURCH WAS BANNED FROM BASEL UP UNTIL THE AGE OF THE HELVETIC REPUBLIC (1798). THIS MEANS THAT FROM 1529 ONWARDS, ATTENDING AND CONDUCTING A CATHOLIC SERVICE WAS OUTLAWED.

COMPARED TO OTHER REFORMED CITIES, HOWEVER, BASEL HAD A FAIRLY LIBERAL REPUTATION. CATHOLICS COULD NOT ACQUIRE REAL ESTATE, NOR DID THEY ENJOY GENERAL CIVIL RIGHTS, BUT THEY WERE NOT PERSECUTED OTHERWISE. SO EVEN AFTER THE REFORMATION, MANY CATHOLICS STILL LIVED IN BASEL. THE CITY'S LIBERAL REPUTATION EXTENDED BEYOND THE CITY'S BOUNDARIES. FOR INSTANCE, ERASMUS RETURNED FROM ROTTERDAM TO BASEL IN 1535 ALTHOUGH HE WAS A PRACTICING CATHOLIC.

IN THE FIELD OF ARCHITECTURE, TOO, THE EFFECTS OF THE REFORMATION WERE NOTICEABLE. WHILE PROTESTANT CHURCHES GENERALLY HAVE QUITE A SOBER AND AUSTERE ATMOSPHERE, CATHOLIC CHURCHES ARE DECORATED MUCH MORE OPULENTLY WITH PAINTINGS AND IMAGES. ARLESHEIM CATHEDRAL, FOR EXAMPLE, HAS SOME BEAUTIFUL CEILING PAINTINGS. IT WAS AGAINST THESE PICTORIAL REPRESENTATION AND THEIR SPLENDOR THAT THE REFORMATION'S ICONOCLASM WAS DIRECTED.

ARLESHEIM

> ASH WEDNESDAY LOST ITS IMPORTANCE IN THE PROTESTANT REGIONS, BUT CARNIVAL CONTINUED TO BE CELEBRATED IN BASEL. THE LOCALS REFUSED TO HAVE THIS FESTIVAL TAKEN AWAY FROM THEM!

ARLESHEIM CATHEDRAL

BASEL MÜNSTER

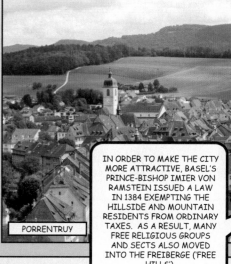

PORRENTRUY

> IN ORDER TO MAKE THE CITY MORE ATTRACTIVE, BASEL'S PRINCE-BISHOP IMIER VON RAMSTEIN ISSUED A LAW IN 1384 EXEMPTING THE HILLSIDE AND MOUNTAIN RESIDENTS FROM ORDINARY TAXES. AS A RESULT, MANY FREE RELIGIOUS GROUPS AND SECTS ALSO MOVED INTO THE FREIBERGE ('FREE HILLS').

CATHOLICS VS REFORMED

THE LEGEND OF ST. URSULA: THIS LEGEND TELLS HOW URSULA AND 11 FEMALE COMPANIONS TRAVELLED UPSTREAM ON THE RHINE. THEIR JOURNEY TOOK THEM TO BASEL, WHERE THEY CONTINUED THEIR PILGRIMAGE TO ROME ON FOOT.

THREE SISTERS, OTTILIE, CHRISCHONA, AND MARGARETHE, SUPPOSEDLY ARRIVED TOGETHER WITH URSULA FROM ROME. EACH BUILT A CHAPEL ON ONE OF THE THREE HILLS SURROUNDING BASEL, AND WITHIN VIEW OF ONE ANOTHER. OTTILIE HAD A CHURCH IN TÖLLINGEN, CHRISCHONA'S CHURCH WAS IN THE PLACE OF THE SAME NAME, AND MARGARETHE HAD A CHURCH IN BINNINGEN SOUTH OF BASEL. WHEN THEY RANG THE CHURCH BELLS, THEY COULD HEAR THE CHIMES FROM THE OTHERS' CHAPELS.

ST. OTTILIE

ST. CHRISCHONA

ST. MARGARETHEN

ST. OTTILIEN CHURCH

THREE SAINTLY SISTERS

ST. MARGARETHEN

ST. CHRISCHONA

CHURCH ARCHITECTURE IN BASEL

PREDIGERKIRCHE

LEONHARDKIRCHE

THE FIRST PETERSKIRCHE CHURCH WAS PROBABLY BUILT IN THE 9TH CENTURY. THIS NEWER BUILDING WAS CONSTRUCTED ON ITS FOUNDATIONS AFTER THE 1356 EARTHQUAKE.

PETERSKIRCHE

BARFÜSSERKIRCHE

THE FIRST MASS OF THE BASEL COUNCIL WAS CELEBRATED HERE IN 1430. TODAY, PREDIGERKIRCHE AT THE DANCE OF DEATH IS ALSO USED BY THE CHRISTIAN CATHOLIC CHURCH, AND FOR CONCERT PERFORMANCES.

...FIRST, COMPLETELY UNIFORM...

THE OLDER CHURCHES ARE ALL BASED ON THE SAME TYPOLOGY

MARTINSKIRCHE AT THE RHEINSPRUNG IS THE OLDEST PARISH CHURCH IN BASEL

MARTINSKIRCHE

CLARAKIRCHE

...AND THEN, A MOTOR OF FANTASTIC ARCHITECTURE!

THE CHURCHYARD AS A THEME OF URBAN DEVELOPMENT

WOW!! BOTH FROM KARL MOSER

SWITZERLAND'S FIRST ALL-CONCRETE CHURCH!

MATTHÄUSKIRCHE, 1895

PAULUS KIRCHE, 1901

ANTONIUSKIRCHE, 1927

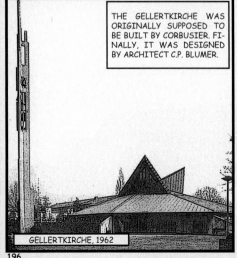

THE GELLERTKIRCHE WAS ORIGINALLY SUPPOSED TO BE BUILT BY CORBUSIER. FINALLY, IT WAS DESIGNED BY ARCHITECT C.P. BLUMER.

GELLERTKIRCHE, 1962

THE PILGRIMAGE CHURCH OF NOTRE DAME DU HAUT AT RONCHAMP IS PROBABLY ONE OF THE WORLD'S MOST IMPORTANT CHURCH BUILDINGS. IT WAS BUILT BY LE CORBUSIER ON THE RUINS OF A CHURCH DESTROYED IN WORLD WAR II.

MY MOTHER ALSO SAID THAT MODERN CHURCHES ARE ARCHITECTURAL INNOVATIONS!

WOW, THAT WAS BUILT BY CORBUSIER!

RONCHAMP, 1954

SHRINKING NUMBER OF CHRISTIANS

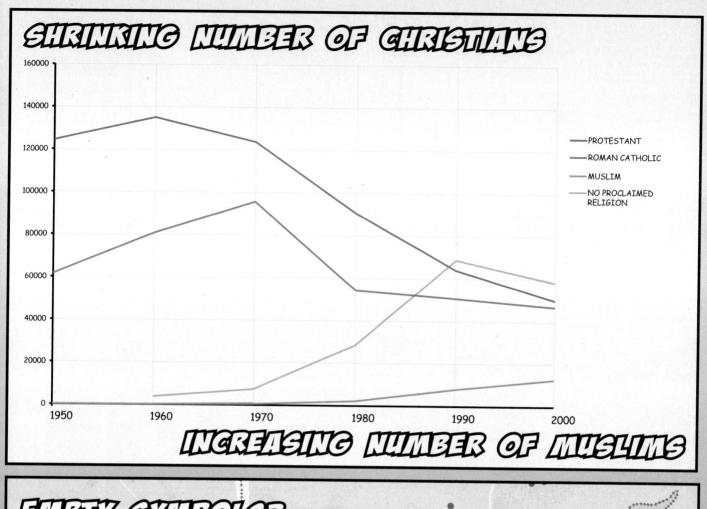

INCREASING NUMBER OF MUSLIMS

EMPTY SYMBOLS?

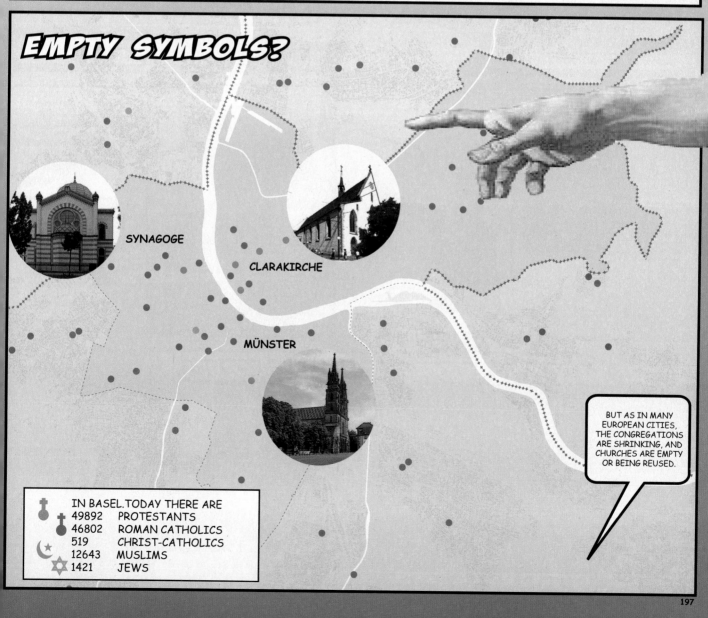

SYNAGOGE

CLARAKIRCHE

MÜNSTER

BUT AS IN MANY EUROPEAN CITIES, THE CONGREGATIONS ARE SHRINKING, AND CHURCHES ARE EMPTY OR BEING REUSED.

IN BASEL TODAY THERE ARE
- 49892 PROTESTANTS
- 46802 ROMAN CATHOLICS
- 519 CHRIST-CATHOLICS
- 12643 MUSLIMS
- 1421 JEWS

JEWS IN BASEL

THE JEWISH COMMUNITY IN BASEL WAS ESTABLISHED FAIRLY EARLY ON. THE FIRST DOCUMENTED REFERENCE TO JEWS IN THE REGION DATES FROM 1216. BUT THEY HAD HARDLY ANY RIGHTS AND WERE SUBJECTED TO ARBITRARY ABUSE BY OTHER CITIZENS. WHEN THE CITY WAS AFFLICTED BY THE PLAGUE IN THE MID-14TH CENTURY, THE JEWS RECEIVED THE BLAME. ON 16 JANUARY 1349, THE JEWS OF BASEL WERE PUT TO DEATH BY FIRE.

NEVERTHELESS, THEY HAD THE COURAGE TO FOUND ANOTHER COMMUNITY JUST A FEW YEARS LATER. BUT IT WAS ALSO SHORT-LIVED. IN 1400, THE JEWS WERE ULTIMATELY EXPELLED FROM THE CITY FOR 400 YEARS.

IT WAS NOT UNTIL THE EN OF THE 19TH CENTURY THA THE JEWS OF BASEL WERE GIV EN FULL CIVIL RIGHTS. THI GAVE THEM THE OPPORTUNIT TO PARTICIPATE IN THE PUB LIC LIFE OF THE CITY AND T PURCHASE REAL ESTATE. TH COMMUNITY GREW RELATIVEL QUICKLY AND ACHIEVED IM PORTANCE BEYOND THE IMME DIATE REGION.

IN THE 1860S, PLANS WERE DE VELOPED FOR THE CONSTRUC TION OF A NEW GREAT SYNA GOGUE FOR THE COMMUNITY. PLOT OF LAND WAS PURCHASE ON WHICH A SYNAGOGUE IN MOORISH-BYZANTINE STYL WAS BUILT, FOLLOWING A DE SIGN BY ARCHITECT HERMAN RUDOLF GAUSS FROM HEIL BRONN. THIS CONSPICUOU BUILDING THUS CONSTITUTE A PUBLIC STRUCTURAL REP RESENTATION OF THE CITY' FREEDOM OF WORSHIP AN LIBERALISM.

HERE WE SEE THE LOCATION OF THE CHURCHES AND THE FIRST SYNAGOGUE IN BASEL IN THE 14TH CENTURY.

IT WAS NOT UNTIL THE YEAR 1800 THAT JEWS RETURNED TO SETTLE IN BASEL. THE EARLY STAGES WERE MARKED BY CAUTION, AND IN THE FIRST HALF OF THE 19TH CENTURY, ONLY 100 TO 200 JEWS LIVED HERE.

THE BASEL SYNAGOGUE WAS BUILT IN 1869 IN THE SO-CALLED MOORISH STYLE. AT THE TIME, THE JEWISH COMMUNITIES IN EUROPE WERE TRYING TO EXPRESS THEIR NEWLY GAINED CIVIL RIGHTS BY WAY OF ARCHIECTURAL STATEMENTS:

THEY EITHER CHOSE THE 'ORIENTAL STYLE' TO SHOWCASE THEIR EMANCIPATION, OR A GOTHIC STYLE TO INDICATE THAT THEIR NEW RIGHTS ALLOWED THEM TO ADOPT THE STYLE OF 'ESTABLISHED SOCIETY'.

SYNAGOGE AT UNTERER HEUBERG (19TH CENT)

THE NEW MAIN SYNAGOGUE AFTER ITS COMPLETION

THE SYNAGOGUE TODAY

IN 1881, THE SYNAGOGUE WAS EXPANDED ONCE MORE, AND THE SEATING DOUBLED FROM 300 TO 600. A SECOND DOME WAS ALSO ADDED TO THE BUILDING.

TODAY, THERE ARE AROUND 2.000 JEWS LIVING IN BASEL. BASEL, TOGETHER WITH ZURICH AND GENEVA, HAS ONE OF THE BIGGEST JEWISH COMMUNITIES IN SWITZERLAND.

BASEL AS THE FOUNDING PLACE OF ISRAEL

BASEL GAINED GLOBAL SIGNIFICANCE THROUGH THE WORLD ZIONIST CONGRESSES HELD IN THE CITY FROM 1897 ONWARDS. THE FIRST CONGRESS (29 TO 31 AUGUST 1897) STATED THE GOAL OF CREATING A SECURE HOME UNDER INTERNATIONAL LAW FOR THE JEWISH PEOPLE IN PALESTINE. AFTER THE CONCLUSION OF THE CONGRESS, HERZL WROTE THE FOLLOWING MEMORABLE WORDS IN HIS DIARY: 'WERE I TO SUM UP THE BASEL CONGRESS IN A WORD – WHICH I SHALL BE CAREFUL NOT TO STATE PUBLICLY – IT WOULD BE THE FOLLOWING: IN BASEL, I FOUNDED THE JEWISH STATE. WERE I TO STATE THIS ALOUD TODAY, THE RESPONSE WOULD BE UNIVERSAL DERISION. PERHAPS IN FIVE YEARS, CERTAINLY IN FIFTY YEARS, ALL WILL ADMIT IT.'

BUT ALTHOUGH THE FOUNDATIONS OF THE STATE OF ISRAEL WERE THUS LAID IN BASEL, THERE IS HARDLY ANY REFERENCE TO THIS EVENT ANYWHERE IN THE CITY. WHY DON'T WE PUT A STATUE OF HERZL ON BARFÜSSERPLATZ?

TAGTE AUF DEN RUF UND UNTER DER LEITUNG VON

DR·THEODOR HERZL
1860–1904

DER ERSTE ZIONISTEN KONGRESS
29–31 AUGUST 1897

UND GRUENDETE DIE ZIONISTISCHE ORGANISATION WEGBEREITERIN DES STAATES ISRAEL

התאסף לקול קריאתו ובהנהגתו של

בנימין זאב תיאודור הרצל

תר״ך – תרס״ד

הקונגרס הציוני הראשון

א-ג אלול תרנ״ז

ויסד את ההסתדרות הציונית העולמית מפלסת הדרך למדינת ישראל

STADTCASINO, VENUE OF THE 1ST WORLD ZIONIST CONGRESS, 1897

THEODOR HERZL (1860-1904), ON THE BALCONY OF THE TROIS ROIS HOTEL, ORGANIZED THE 1ST WORLD ZIONIST CONGRESS.

MUSLIMS IN BASEL

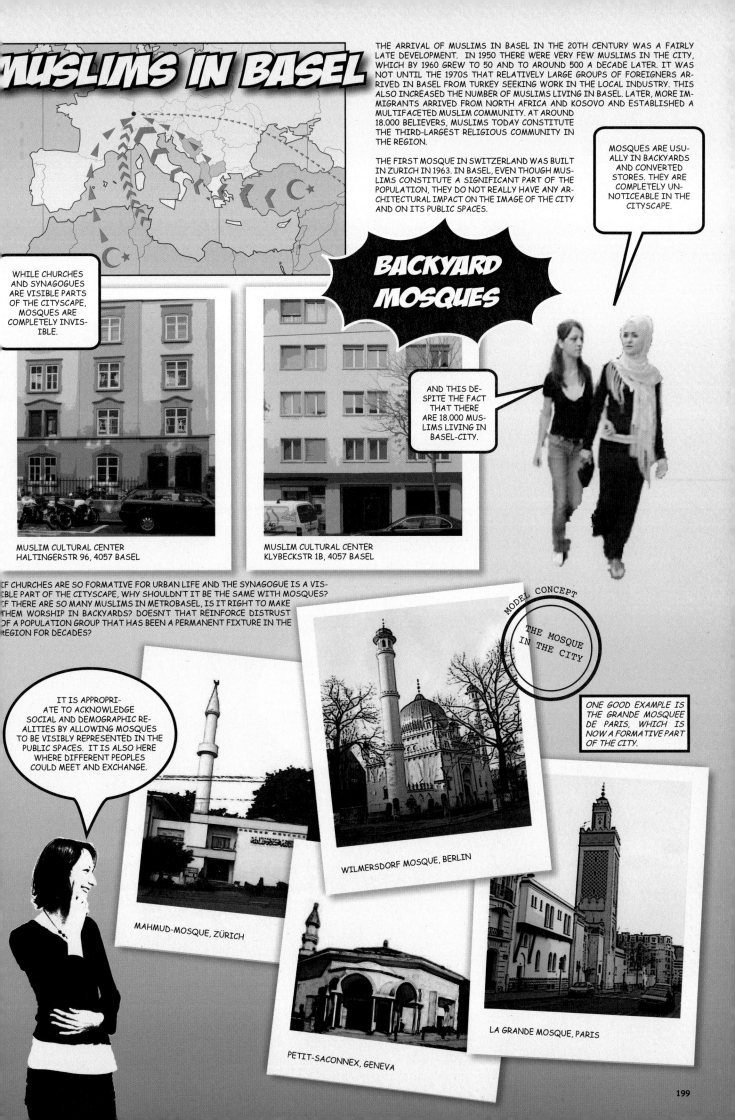

THE ARRIVAL OF MUSLIMS IN BASEL IN THE 20TH CENTURY WAS A FAIRLY LATE DEVELOPMENT. IN 1950 THERE WERE VERY FEW MUSLIMS IN THE CITY, WHICH BY 1960 GREW TO 50 AND TO AROUND 500 A DECADE LATER. IT WAS NOT UNTIL THE 1970S THAT RELATIVELY LARGE GROUPS OF FOREIGNERS ARRIVED IN BASEL FROM TURKEY SEEKING WORK IN THE LOCAL INDUSTRY. THIS ALSO INCREASED THE NUMBER OF MUSLIMS LIVING IN BASEL. LATER, MORE IMMIGRANTS ARRIVED FROM NORTH AFRICA AND KOSOVO AND ESTABLISHED A MULTIFACETED MUSLIM COMMUNITY. AT AROUND 18.000 BELIEVERS, MUSLIMS TODAY CONSTITUTE THE THIRD-LARGEST RELIGIOUS COMMUNITY IN THE REGION.

THE FIRST MOSQUE IN SWITZERLAND WAS BUILT IN ZURICH IN 1963. IN BASEL, EVEN THOUGH MUSLIMS CONSTITUTE A SIGNIFICANT PART OF THE POPULATION, THEY DO NOT REALLY HAVE ANY ARCHITECTURAL IMPACT ON THE IMAGE OF THE CITY AND ON ITS PUBLIC SPACES.

MOSQUES ARE USUALLY IN BACKYARDS AND CONVERTED STORES. THEY ARE COMPLETELY UNNOTICEABLE IN THE CITYSCAPE.

WHILE CHURCHES AND SYNAGOGUES ARE VISIBLE PARTS OF THE CITYSCAPE, MOSQUES ARE COMPLETELY INVISIBLE.

BACKYARD MOSQUES

AND THIS DESPITE THE FACT THAT THERE ARE 18.000 MUSLIMS LIVING IN BASEL-CITY.

MUSLIM CULTURAL CENTER
HALTINGERSTR 96, 4057 BASEL

MUSLIM CULTURAL CENTER
KLYBECKSTR 1B, 4057 BASEL

IF CHURCHES ARE SO FORMATIVE FOR URBAN LIFE AND THE SYNAGOGUE IS A VISIBLE PART OF THE CITYSCAPE, WHY SHOULDN'T IT BE THE SAME WITH MOSQUES? IF THERE ARE SO MANY MUSLIMS IN METROBASEL, IS IT RIGHT TO MAKE THEM WORSHIP IN BACKYARDS? DOESN'T THAT REINFORCE DISTRUST OF A POPULATION GROUP THAT HAS BEEN A PERMANENT FIXTURE IN THE REGION FOR DECADES?

MODEL CONCEPT

THE MOSQUE IN THE CITY

ONE GOOD EXAMPLE IS THE GRANDE MOSQUEE DE PARIS, WHICH IS NOW A FORMATIVE PART OF THE CITY.

IT IS APPROPRIATE TO ACKNOWLEDGE SOCIAL AND DEMOGRAPHIC REALITIES BY ALLOWING MOSQUES TO BE VISIBLY REPRESENTED IN THE PUBLIC SPACES. IT IS ALSO HERE WHERE DIFFERENT PEOPLES COULD MEET AND EXCHANGE.

WILMERSDORF MOSQUE, BERLIN

MAHMUD-MOSQUE, ZÜRICH

LA GRANDE MOSQUE, PARIS

PETIT-SACONNEX, GENEVA

BASEL HAS ALWAYS BEEN A LIVELY AND OPEN CITY THAT HAS INTEGRATED AND BECOME HOME TO PEOPLE OF FOREIGN ORIGINS AND RELIGIONS. A MOSQUE IN BASEL WOULD BE AND ARCHITECTURAL AND URBANISTIC EXPRESSION OF THE PRESENCE OF AN IMPORTANT POPULATION GROUP WITHIN THE CITYSCAPE.

JOHANN LUDWIG BURCKHARDT AKA SCHEICH IBRAHIM (1784-1817) WAS THE FIRST EUROPEAN TO MAKE THE HAJJ (PILGRIMAGE) TO MECCA

THE MOSQUE OF BASEL

RECREATION IN METRO BASEL

METROBASEL IS SITUATED IN A UNIQUE LOCATION WITHIN EUROPE, AT THE JUNCTURE OF THREE VERY DIFFERENT GEOGRAPHIC REGIONS: THE JURA, THE VOSGES, AND THE BLACK FOREST.

FUMIKO IS A GRADUATE STUDENT AT ETH STUDIO BASEL DOING RESEARCH ON THE TOPIC OF 'URBAN NATURE'...

IT'S A LOVELY SUNDAY AFTERNOON AND MICHEL'S LAST DAY IN BASEL. PATRICIA HAS PLANNED A LOVELY TOUR AROUND BASEL. SHE WANTS TO START IN THE JURA, WHERE ONE OF THE FIVE 'BELCHEN' SUMMITS OFFERS A VIEW OF THE ENTIRE REGION AND OF THE OTHER MOUNTAINS THAT ARE ALSO NAMED 'BELCHEN'S.

*DEFINITION VOSGES:
THE TERM 'SUNDGAU' IS USED TO REFER TO THE TOPOGRAPHICAL REGION BETWEEN BASEL AND MULHOUSE. IT IS THE SOUTHERNMOST PART OF ALSACE. TO THE WEST, IT IS BORDERED BY THE VOSGES, A LOW MOUNTAIN RANGE WITH FOOTHILLS REACHING INTO THE SUNDGAU REGION. DUE TO OVERLAP, THE THREE TERMS ARE OCCASIONALLY INTERCHANGED. WHILE 'VOSGES' AND 'SUNDGAU' ARE DESIGNATIONS FOR GEOGRAPHICAL AREAS, 'ALSACE' ALSO REFERS TO A POLITICAL UNIT: IT IS ONE OF THE REGIONS (TERRITORIAL AUTHORITIES) OF FRANCE. IN THE FOLLOWING, WE WILL PRIMARILY MAKE REFERENCE TO THE VOSGES.

PATRICIA AND MICHEL MEET ROLF D'AUJOURD'HUI ON THE BELCHEN. HE WAS BASEL'S CANTONAL ARCHEOLOGIST FROM 1982-1998. NOW HE WORKS WITH CHRISTINE HATZ ON A RESEARCH PROJECT ABOUT THE BELCHEN SYSTEM – A TOPIC HE HAS LONG BEEN INTERESTED IN.

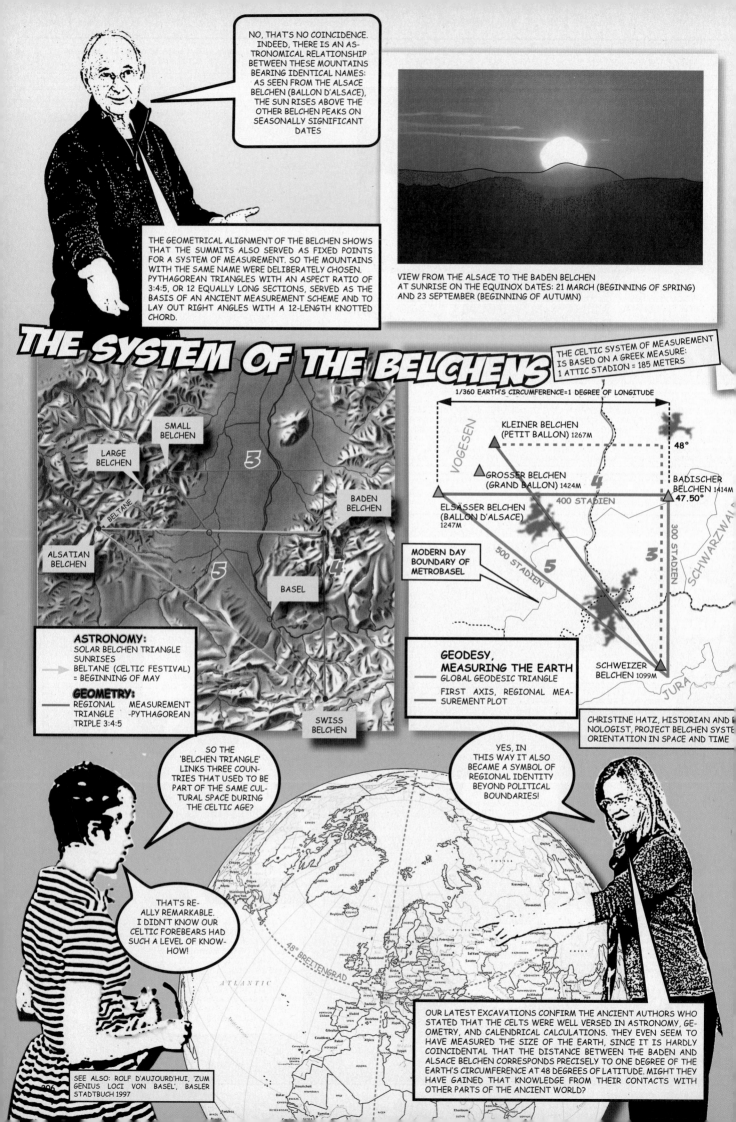

NO, THAT'S NO COINCIDENCE. INDEED, THERE IS AN ASTRONOMICAL RELATIONSHIP BETWEEN THESE MOUNTAINS BEARING IDENTICAL NAMES: AS SEEN FROM THE ALSACE BELCHEN (BALLON D'ALSACE), THE SUN RISES ABOVE THE OTHER BELCHEN PEAKS ON SEASONALLY SIGNIFICANT DATES

THE GEOMETRICAL ALIGNMENT OF THE BELCHEN SHOWS THAT THE SUMMITS ALSO SERVED AS FIXED POINTS FOR A SYSTEM OF MEASUREMENT. SO THE MOUNTAINS WITH THE SAME NAME WERE DELIBERATELY CHOSEN. PYTHAGOREAN TRIANGLES WITH AN ASPECT RATIO OF 3:4:5, OR 12 EQUALLY LONG SECTIONS, SERVED AS THE BASIS OF AN ANCIENT MEASUREMENT SCHEME AND TO LAY OUT RIGHT ANGLES WITH A 12-LENGTH KNOTTED CHORD.

VIEW FROM THE ALSACE TO THE BADEN BELCHEN AT SUNRISE ON THE EQUINOX DATES: 21 MARCH (BEGINNING OF SPRING) AND 23 SEPTEMBER (BEGINNING OF AUTUMN)

THE SYSTEM OF THE BELCHENS

THE CELTIC SYSTEM OF MEASUREMENT IS BASED ON A GREEK MEASURE: 1 ATTIC STADION = 185 METERS

SMALL BELCHEN

LARGE BELCHEN

BELTANE

ALSATIAN BELCHEN

BADEN BELCHEN

BASEL

SWISS BELCHEN

ASTRONOMY:
SOLAR BELCHEN TRIANGLE SUNRISES
BELTANE (CELTIC FESTIVAL) = BEGINNING OF MAY

GEOMETRY:
REGIONAL MEASUREMENT TRIANGLE -PYTHAGOREAN TRIPLE 3:4:5

1/360 EARTH'S CIRCUMFERENCE=1 DEGREE OF LONGITUDE

VOGESEN

KLEINER BELCHEN (PETIT BALLON) 1267M

48°

GROSSER BELCHEN (GRAND BALLON) 1424M

BADISCHER BELCHEN 1414M

47.50°

ELSÄSSER BELCHEN (BALLON D'ALSACE) 1247M

400 STADIEN

MODERN DAY BOUNDARY OF METROBASEL

500 STADIEN

300 STADIEN

SCHWARZWALD

SCHWEIZER BELCHEN 1099M

JURA

GEODESY, MEASURING THE EARTH
GLOBAL GEODESIC TRIANGLE
FIRST AXIS, REGIONAL MEASUREMENT PLOT

CHRISTINE HATZ, HISTORIAN AND [...]NOLOGIST, PROJECT BELCHEN SYSTE[...] ORIENTATION IN SPACE AND TIME

SO THE 'BELCHEN TRIANGLE' LINKS THREE COUNTRIES THAT USED TO BE PART OF THE SAME CULTURAL SPACE DURING THE CELTIC AGE?

YES, IN THIS WAY IT ALSO BECAME A SYMBOL OF REGIONAL IDENTITY BEYOND POLITICAL BOUNDARIES!

THAT'S REALLY REMARKABLE. I DIDN'T KNOW OUR CELTIC FOREBEARS HAD SUCH A LEVEL OF KNOW-HOW!

48° BREITENGRAD

ATLANTIC

SEE ALSO: ROLF D'AUJOURD'HUI, 'ZUM GENIUS LOCI VON BASEL', BASLER STADTBUCH 1997

OUR LATEST EXCAVATIONS CONFIRM THE ANCIENT AUTHORS WHO STATED THAT THE CELTS WERE WELL VERSED IN ASTRONOMY, GEOMETRY, AND CALENDRICAL CALCULATIONS. THEY EVEN SEEM TO HAVE MEASURED THE SIZE OF THE EARTH, SINCE IT IS HARDLY COINCIDENTAL THAT THE DISTANCE BETWEEN THE BADEN AND ALSACE BELCHEN CORRESPONDS PRECISELY TO ONE DEGREE OF THE EARTH'S CIRCUMFERENCE AT 48 DEGREES OF LATITUDE. MIGHT THEY HAVE GAINED THAT KNOWLEDGE FROM THEIR CONTACTS WITH OTHER PARTS OF THE ANCIENT WORLD?

MARKUS RITTER, FORMER COUNCIL PRESIDENT OF BASEL-CITY AND BIOLOGIST, IS TALKING ABOUT THE THREE TOPOGRAPHIC REGIONS OF METROBASEL.

ROMAN TIMES

999-1529
DIOCESE OF BASEL

1529: REFORMATION
BISHOP IN PORRENTRUY

1813
'H RULE

1815-1978
CANTON OF BERNE

SEIT 1978
CANTON OF JURA

IN 1384, IMIER OF RAMSTEIN, THE BISHOP OF BASEL, RELIEVED THE RESIDENTS OF THE JURA LIVING IN AREAS ABOVE 1000 M FROM ALL TAX DUTIES AND INTRODUCED FREEDOM OF WORSHIP.

DELEMONT

...THE FRENCH-SPEAKING REGION OF JURA IS MAINLY CATHOLIC, UNLIKE BASEL, WHICH IS PROTESTANT. TRACES CAN BE FOUND IN ITS CULTURE AS WELL AS IN ITS ARCHITECTURE.

MAP OF THE THREE GEOGRAPHIC REGIONS OF METROBASEL

BLACK FOREST

VOSGES

THE JURA

JURA

....AS SEEN FROM BASEL, THE JURA IS THE RANGE OF MOUNTAINS LEADING UP TO THE ALPS. IN GEOLOGICAL TERMS, THIS IS MORE OR LESS THE WAY THE LANDSCAPE DEVELOPED: THE ALPS WERE PILED UP AGAINST THE BARRIER OF THE VOSGES AND THE BLACK FOREST.

THE NAME 'JURA' IS A CELTIC WORD MEANING 'WOODLAND', MOST LIKELY DUE TO THE DENSE TREE COVER ON ITS SLOPES.

THE PHENOLOGICAL FLOWER INDEX SHOWS CLEARLY WHICH PLANTS ARE NATIVE TO THE REGION.

PLANTS NATIVE TO THE JURA AND THEIR BLOSSOMING PERIODS

ST LUCIE CHERRY
PRUNUS MAHALEB
(APRIL-MAI)

COMMON BEECH
FAGUS SYLVATICA
(SEPT)

YELLO GENTIAN
GENTIANA LUTEN
(JULI-AUG)

COTONEASTER
COTONEASTER
(JUNI)

MARKUS RITTER IS A BIOLOGIST AND WAS THE PRESIDENT OF THE CANTONAL PARLIAMENT OF BASEL-CITY IN 2000.

*PHENOLOGY: THE STUDY OF RECURRING NATURAL BIOLOGICAL PROCESSES, I.E., THE GROWTH, BLOOM, AND CYCLE OF SEASONS IN PLANTS.

THE NAME 'SUNDGAU' IS DERIVED FROM THE EARLY MEDIEVAL SUBDIVISION OF ALSACE INTO A NORTHERN AND A SOUTHERN 'GAU', OR SHIRE. AT THE TIME, THE SUNDGAU ENCOMPASSED PARTS OF JURA IN THE SOUTH AND REACHED WESTWARDS BEYOND BELFORT INTO THE VOSGES. SINCE A REFORM OF TERRITORIAL ADMINISTRATION IN 1871, IT HAS BEEN USED TO DESCRIBE THE MODERN-DAY REGION BETWEEN MULHOUSE AND BASEL

GREAT CYCLING TOUR!!!!

THE REGION IS CRISSCROSSED BY MANY CANALS AND RIVERBEDS

THIS IS A TYPICAL SUNDGAU VILLAGE WITH TIMBER-FRAMED HOUSES. THESE VILLAGES ARE GROWING FAIRLY QUICKLY NOW, AND ARE IN DANGER OF LOSING THEIR IDENTITY. IT IS A CREEPING SUBURBANIZATION PROCESS.

MAP OF THE THREE LANDSCAPE REGIONS OF METROBASEL

BLACK FOREST

SUNDGAU

JURA

SUNDGAU USED TO BE REGARDED AS THE BREADBASKET OF BASEL. MOST OF BASEL'S FOOD CAME FROM THIS REGION. BASEL'S CONNECTION TO THE SUNDGAU WAS IN A WAY MORE IMPORTANT THAN THE LINK TO THE REST OF SWITZERLAND.

THE SUNDGAU

HISTORICALLY, THE AGRICULTURAL BASE OF THE REGION HAS GIVEN RISE TO STRONG TRADE AND EXCHANGE BETWEEN THE FRENCH AND ALEMANNIC PEOPLES. IN A LONGSTANDING TRADITION, MOST PEOPLE ARE RAISED BILINGUALLY

THIS CAN ALSO BE SEEN IN THE BASEL CITY GATES: THE SPALENTOR, WHICH LEADS OUT TO ST LOUIS AND THE SUNDGAU, IS THE MOST BEAUTIFUL AND MOST OPULENTLY DECORATED OF ALL THE GATES IN THE BASEL CITY WALL.

SPALENTOR

PLANTS NATIVE TO THE SUNDGAU AND THEIR BLOSSOMING PERIODS

CORN POPPY
PAPAVER RHOEAS
(APR-AUG)

HONEY CLOVER
MELILOTUS ALBUS
(JULI-AUG)

EVENING PRIMROSE
OENOTHERA BIENNIS
(JUNI-SEPT)

HAWKWEED OXTONGUE
PICRIS HIERACIOIDES
(JULI-OKT)

THE BLACK FOREST, NORTHEAST OF BASEL, IS KNOWN AS AN AREA OF UNSPOILED NATURE AND RECREATION

THE STEEP SLOPES ON THE EASTERN SIDE OF THE RHINE RIFT, TOGETHER WITH SPECIFIC TYPES OF SOIL, CREATE A LOCAL FLORA FEATURING VERY SPECIAL PLANTS.

THE BLACK FOREST MOUNTAINS ARE A POPULAR HIKING AREA.

TITISEE

FROM THE MOUNTAIN-TOPS OF THE BLACK FOREST, SUCH AS THE FELDBERG SHOWN HERE, STUPENDOUS VIEWS OF THE MOUNTAIN LAKES IN THE VALLEYS CAN BE ENJOYED.

MAP OF THE THREE LANDSCAPE REGIONS OF METROBASEL

BLACK FOREST

SUNDGAU

JURA

Wanderkarte
Maßstab 1:30 000
Mit Radwegen
Freiburg-Ost

SCHWARZWALD
Mit farbigen Wegezeichen und Wanderwegebeschreibung von
Freiburg · Buchenbach · Glottertal
Gundelfingen · Hinterzarten · Kirchzarten
Oberried · St. Märgen · St. Peter · Siegen

THE BLACK FOREST

NAMED FOR ITS DARK CONIFERS, IT WAS A PLACE RENOWNED FOR THE MYTHICAL AND THE SUPERNATURAL UNTIL THE ROMANTIC WRITERS OF THE 19TH CENTURY USED IT AS THE SETTING FOR THEIR FAIRYTALES.

THE BLACK FOREST IS ALSO FAMED FOR ITS TRADITION, ITS CRAFTS, AND ITS CUISINE. CUCKOO CLOCKS ARE VERY POPULAR WITH TOURISTS, AND THE LOCAL SMOKED HAM HAS A FINE, STRONG FLAVOR.

BUT OF COURSE OUR FAVORITE IS THE BLACK FOREST CAKE. MMMMMMHH!!!!

PLANTS NATIVE TO THE BLACK FOREST AND THEIR BLOSSOMING PERIODS

SCHWEFEL-ANEMONE
ANEMONE SULPHEREA
(MAI-OKT)

ALPINE LOVAGE
LIGUSTICUM MUTELLINA
(JUNI-AUG)

EUROPEAN SIVER FIR
PICEA ABIES
(NOV-FEB)

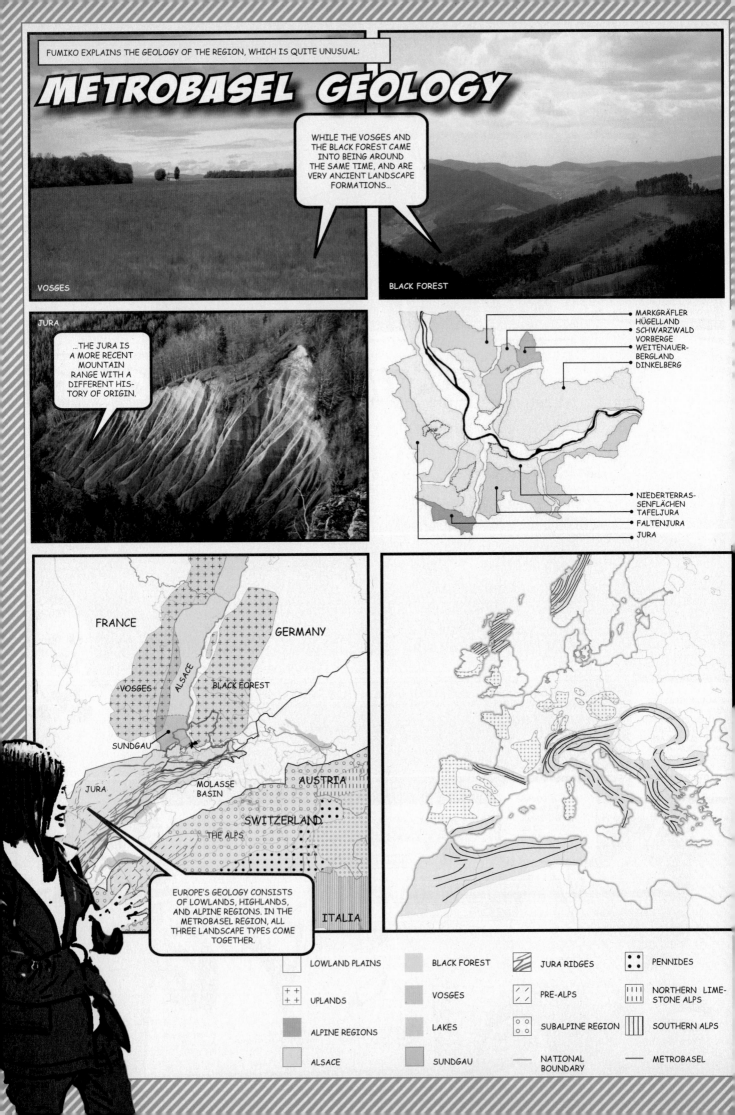

RECREATION IN THE REGION...

HERE WE SEE THE EXISTING PLACES OF RECREATION IN THE REGION.

THEY CONSTITUTE A NETWORK OF REGIONAL LEISURE FACILITIES.

THE RHINE

+ THEMAL BATH
+ WELLNESS CENTER

◆ WINTERSPORT
◆ MOUNTAIN BIKE

● WATER SPORT
● GOLF
● SPORT
● BIKE RENTAL

CANOEING AND WHITEWATER RAFTING IN HUNINGUE

THE VOSGES

OR CYCLING THROUGH THE HILLS OF THE VOSGES

SWIMMING IN THE RHINE, BASEL

CYCLING IN THE VOSGES

THE JURA

... HIKING... THERE IS NO END TO THE HIKING TRAILS THROUGHOUT THE ENTIRE REGION...

WANDERN IM JURA

PATRICIA SUGGESTS THAT THEY TAKE A TRAIN OUT OF TOWN FOR A LITTLE RECREATION AND TO EXPLORE THE REGION...

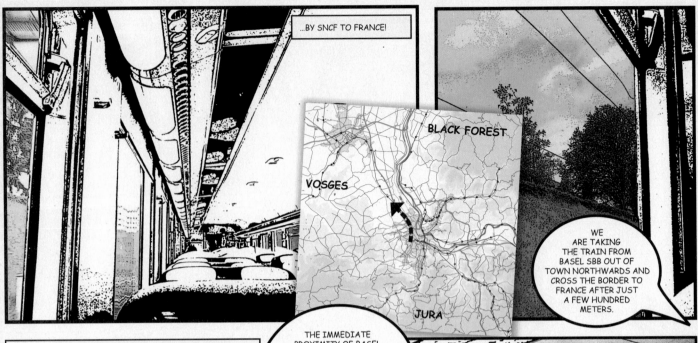

...BY SNCF TO FRANCE!

BLACK FOREST

VOSGES

JURA

WE ARE TAKING THE TRAIN FROM BASEL SBB OUT OF TOWN NORTHWARDS AND CROSS THE BORDER TO FRANCE AFTER JUST A FEW HUNDRED METERS.

PATRICIA IS LOOKING FORWARD TO SHOWING MICHEL HOW CLOSE BASEL IS TO THE THREE REGIONS...

THE IMMEDIATE PROXIMITY OF BASEL TO THE THREE REGIONS OF THE JURA, THE BLACK FOREST, AND THE VOSGES IS UNIQUE IN EUROPE. FEW OTHER CITIES ARE AS CLOSELY LINKED TO DIVERSE LANDSCAPE AREAS.

THE VOSGES

THE SUNDGAU

ON THE LEFT, WE SEE THE FOOTHILLS OF THE VOSGES STRETCHING OUT INTO THE SUNDGAU.

THE BLACK FOREST

TO THE RIGHT, WE SEE THE HEIGHTS OF THE BLACK FOREST IN THE BACKGROUND. IN BETWEEN LIES THE RHINE, WHICH LINKS THE ENTIRE REGION.

AND WHAT IS THIS LAKE AREA WE ARE PASSING THROUGH?

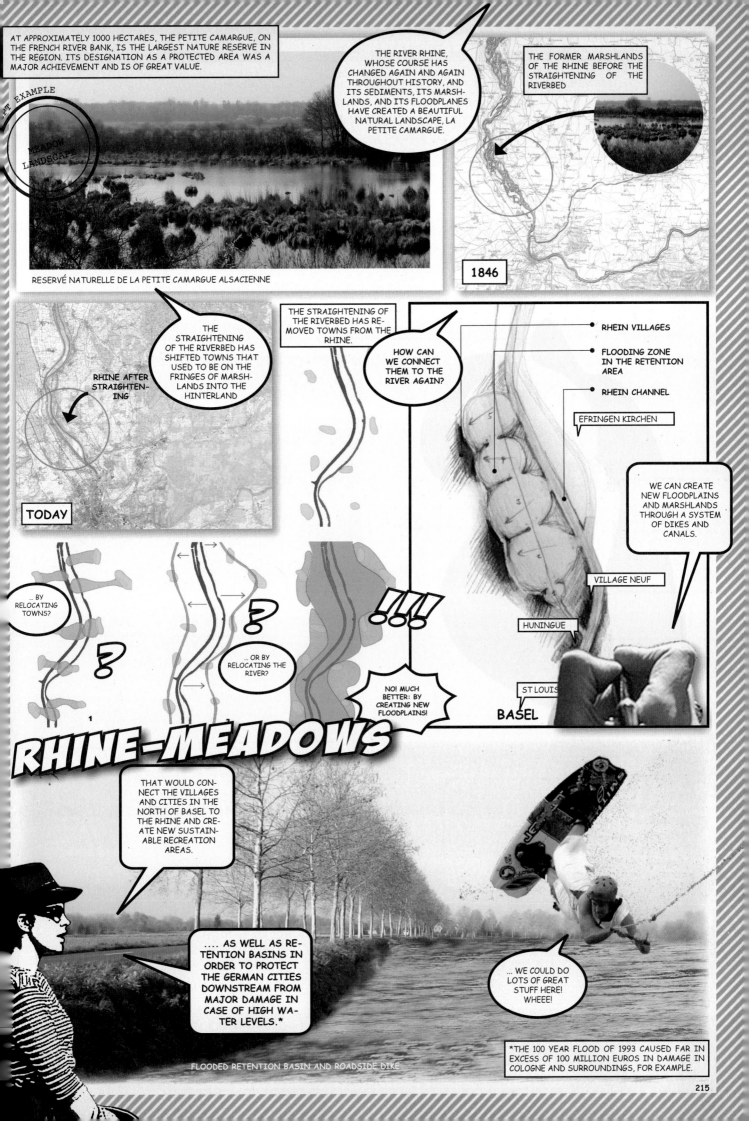

AT APPROXIMATELY 1000 HECTARES, THE PETITE CAMARGUE, ON THE FRENCH RIVER BANK, IS THE LARGEST NATURE RESERVE IN THE REGION. ITS DESIGNATION AS A PROTECTED AREA WAS A MAJOR ACHIEVEMENT AND IS OF GREAT VALUE.

PT EXAMPLE

MEADOW LANDSCAPE

THE RIVER RHINE, WHOSE COURSE HAS CHANGED AGAIN AND AGAIN THROUGHOUT HISTORY, AND ITS SEDIMENTS, ITS MARSHLANDS, AND ITS FLOODPLANES HAVE CREATED A BEAUTIFUL NATURAL LANDSCAPE, LA PETITE CAMARGUE.

THE FORMER MARSHLANDS OF THE RHINE BEFORE THE STRAIGHTENING OF THE RIVERBED

1846

RESERVÉ NATURELLE DE LA PETITE CAMARGUE ALSACIENNE

THE STRAIGHTENING OF THE RIVERBED HAS SHIFTED TOWNS THAT USED TO BE ON THE FRINGES OF MARSHLANDS INTO THE HINTERLAND

RHINE AFTER STRAIGHTENING

TODAY

THE STRAIGHTENING OF THE RIVERBED HAS REMOVED TOWNS FROM THE RHINE.

HOW CAN WE CONNECT THEM TO THE RIVER AGAIN?

RHEIN VILLAGES

FLOODING ZONE IN THE RETENTION AREA

RHEIN CHANNEL

EFRINGEN KIRCHEN

WE CAN CREATE NEW FLOODPLAINS AND MARSHLANDS THROUGH A SYSTEM OF DIKES AND CANALS.

... BY RELOCATING TOWNS?

... OR BY RELOCATING THE RIVER?

NO! MUCH BETTER: BY CREATING NEW FLOODPLAINS!

VILLAGE NEUF

HUNINGUE

ST LOUIS

BASEL

RHINE-MEADOWS

THAT WOULD CONNECT THE VILLAGES AND CITIES IN THE NORTH OF BASEL TO THE RHINE AND CREATE NEW SUSTAINABLE RECREATION AREAS.

.... AS WELL AS RETENTION BASINS IN ORDER TO PROTECT THE GERMAN CITIES DOWNSTREAM FROM MAJOR DAMAGE IN CASE OF HIGH WATER LEVELS.*

... WE COULD DO LOTS OF GREAT STUFF HERE! WHEEE!

FLOODED RETENTION BASIN AND ROADSIDE DIKE

*THE 100 YEAR FLOOD OF 1993 CAUSED FAR IN EXCESS OF 100 MILLION EUROS IN DAMAGE IN COLOGNE AND SURROUNDINGS, FOR EXAMPLE.

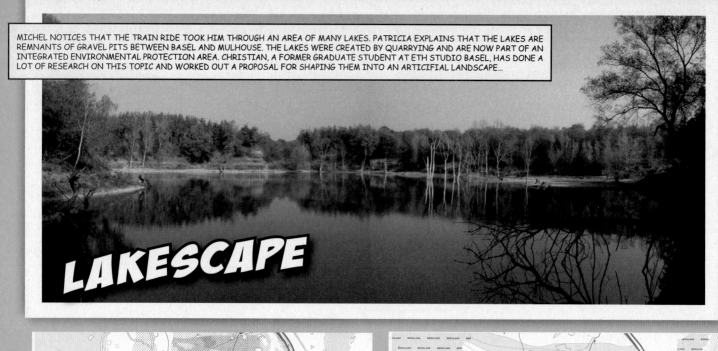

MICHEL NOTICES THAT THE TRAIN RIDE TOOK HIM THROUGH AN AREA OF MANY LAKES. PATRICIA EXPLAINS THAT THE LAKES ARE REMNANTS OF GRAVEL PITS BETWEEN BASEL AND MULHOUSE. THE LAKES WERE CREATED BY QUARRYING AND ARE NOW PART OF AN INTEGRATED ENVIRONMENTAL PROTECTION AREA. CHRISTIAN, A FORMER GRADUATE STUDENT AT ETH STUDIO BASEL, HAS DONE A LOT OF RESEARCH ON THIS TOPIC AND WORKED OUT A PROPOSAL FOR SHAPING THEM INTO AN ARTICIFIAL LANDSCAPE...

LAKESCAPE

THE WATER IN THESE LAKES IS PART OF A HUGE SUBTERRANEAN AQUIFER THAT FORMS A SECOND, INVISIBLE TOPOGRAPHY BELOW THE VISIBLE TOPOGRAPHY OF THE EARTH.

THE GROUNDWATER SYSTEM IN THE UPPER RHINE RIFT WITH ITS DIFFERENT WATER LEVELS

THIS IS A CLOSE-UP OF ONE SUCH LAKE. IT IS INTERESTING TO SEE HOW TECHNICAL AND INDUSTRIAL DEVELOPMENT CAN CREATE SOMETHING SO BEAUTIFUL. WHY AREN'T THERE MORE PLACES LIKE THIS?

LAKESCAPE

CHRISTIAN DEVELOPED THIS PROJECT FOR HIS DIPLOMA THESIS AT ETH STUDIO BASEL...

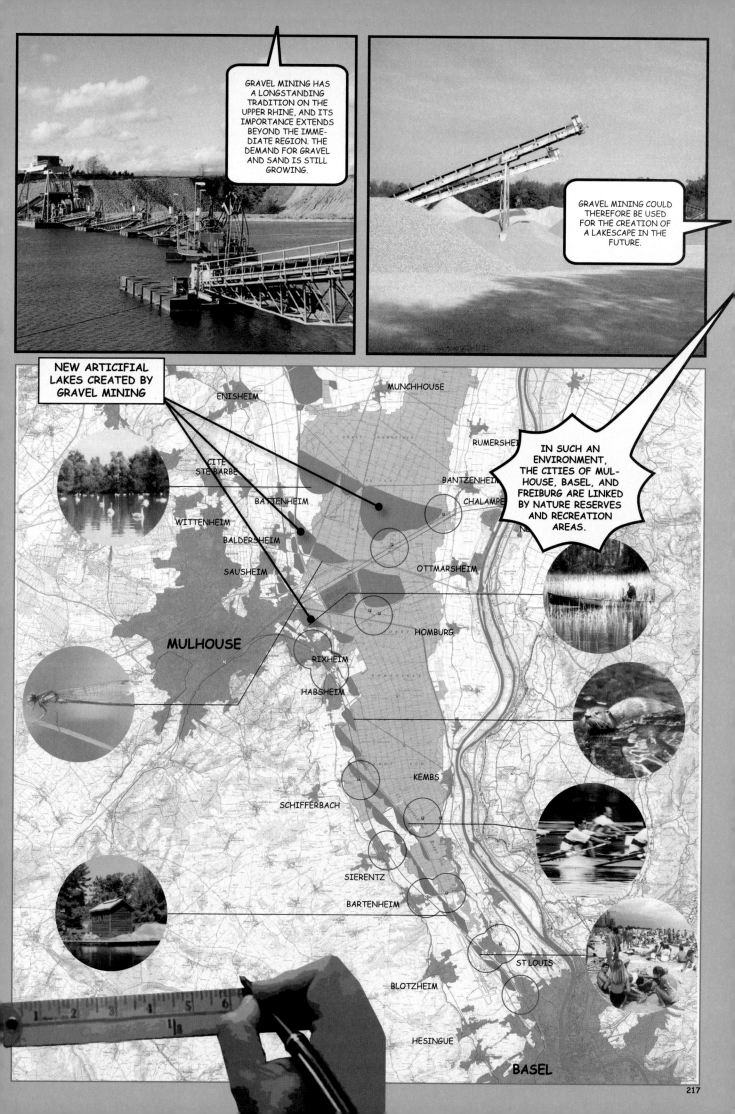

GRAVEL MINING HAS A LONGSTANDING TRADITION ON THE UPPER RHINE, AND ITS IMPORTANCE EXTENDS BEYOND THE IMMEDIATE REGION. THE DEMAND FOR GRAVEL AND SAND IS STILL GROWING.

GRAVEL MINING COULD THEREFORE BE USED FOR THE CREATION OF A LAKESCAPE IN THE FUTURE.

NEW ARTICIFIAL LAKES CREATED BY GRAVEL MINING

IN SUCH AN ENVIRONMENT, THE CITIES OF MULHOUSE, BASEL, AND FREIBURG ARE LINKED BY NATURE RESERVES AND RECREATION AREAS.

217

A NEW LAKESCAPE THAT CAN BE CREATED THROUGH GRAVEL MINING OVER TIME.

WOW!! I LOVE THE IDEA OF A LAKESCAPE MASTERPLAN FOR THE METROPOLITAN REGION OF BASEL-MULHOUSE-FREIBURG.
LIKE CENTRAL PARK IN MANHATTAN, A PIECE OF NATURE WOULD DEFINE A CENTER WHERE CITY RESIDENTS CAN MEET FOR RECREATION.

IN THE CITY CENTER OF BASEL, THE RHINE IS ACTIVELY USED FOR RECREATION AND LEISURE ACTIVITIES.

IN THE SURROUNDING AREAS, ON THE OTHER HAND, ITS POTENTIAL IS HARDLY USED AT ALL. OFTEN, THE RIVER BANK ISN'T EVEN ACCESSIBLE.

THE RHINE

THE RHINE BEFORE ITS CANALIZATION

WOW, LOOK AT THIS GREAT VIEW. IT'S JUST BEAUTIFUL!

SINCE TIME IMMEMORIAL, THE RHINE HAS IMPARTED A VERY SPECIAL CHARACTER TO BASEL AND ITS ENVIRONS AND SHAPED MANY CULTURAL DEVELOPMENTS THERE...

THE CANALIZATION OF THE RHINE BEGAN IN 1846. THE RIVER WAS FORCED INTO AN ARTIFICIAL RIVERBED. ALTHOUGH RATIONALIZATION AND EFFICIENCY WERE ENHANCED, NATURAL BEAUTY WAS LOST...

BUT PEOPLE ALSO BEGAN TO USE THE RHINE AS A SOURCE OF ENERGY: THE HYDROPOWER STATION AT RHEINFELDEN, BUILT IN 1898, IS THE OLDEST RIVER POWER PLANT IN EUROPE. SINCE THEN, ANOTHER SIX POWER STATIONS HAVE BEEN CONSTRUCTED IN THE REGION, SUPPLYING METROBASEL WITH GREEN ELECTRICITY. SEVERE INTERVENTIONS IN THE NATURAL ENVIRONMENT CAN ALSO BE VERY SUSTAINABLE.

THE POWER STATION AT ON THE RHINE AT BIRSFELDEN HAS CREATED AN ARTIFICIAL LAKE IN THE RIVER, WHICH CAN BE USED FOR SPORTS AND RECREATION.

OTTMARSHEIM, 1928

KEMBS, 1928

PETIT CAMARGUE NATURE RESERVE

RHEINFELDEN, 1898

BIRSFELDEN POWER STATION 1954

AUGST WYHLEN, 1907

TODAY

FUMIKO DESCRIBES HOW NATURE IS ALSO AN ENVIRONMENT SHAPED BY HUMANS -- FOR EXAMPLE, IN ORDER TO ENABLE SUSTAINABLE LIVING OR TO GENERATE POWER.

NATURE AND RECREATION ARE LINKED TO SUSTAINABILITY AND ENERGY.

THE BEAUTIFUL POWER PLANT OF BIRSFELDEN WAS BUILT IN 1951 BY ZURICH ARCHITECT HANS HOFMANN. THE TRANSPARENCY AND EXPRESSIVE FORM OF THE BUILDING ARE CAPTIVATING. IT IS LOCATED RIGHT ON THE BORDER BETWEEN BASEL-CITY AND BASEL-COUNTRY, AND SUPPLIES NEARLY 17% OF THE ENERGY CONSUMED IN THE ENTIRE REGION.

POWERSTATION KEMBS

OLLIE IS ANOTHER FORMER STUDENT AT ETH STUDIO BASEL.

WEHR RESERVOIR

LANDSCAPE AND ENERGY

HORNBERG RESERVOIR

MANY PLACES WHERE HUMANS HAVE INTERVENED TO SHAPE THE NATURAL ENVIRONMENT ARE INCREDIBLY BEAUTIFUL. ALMOST BREATHTAKING.

RESERVOIRS ARE BUILT TO BALANCE OUT CYCLICAL VARIATIONS IN ENERGY CONSUMPTION.*

NEW RESERVOIRS

WHY DON'T WE BUILD ADDITIONAL MOUNTAIN LAKES THAT STORE AND GENERATE ENERGY AND CAN BE USED FOR RECREATION AT THE SAME TIME?

△ BLAUEN

△ AMEISENBUCK

HOHEWILDSE

WILDSBERG

MALSBURG

NEW RESERVOIR KANDERN

BAD RIEDLINGEN

KANDERN

HOLZEN

MAPPACH

MAUGENHA D

EGRINGEN

WITTLINGEN

OHH... THEN WE COULD GO FOR NICE WALKS ALONG THE BASEL ALSTER IN THE SUMMER...

*RESERVOIRS ARE BUILT ON MOUNTAINTOPS. WATER IS PUMPED INTO THEM FROM A LOWER LEVEL, WHICH TAKES ENERGY. WHEN THIS ENERGY IS REQUIRED FOR USE, THE WATER IS RELEASED FROM THE RESERVOIR TO FLOW BACK DOWNHILL THROUGH TURBINES THAT CONVERT THE WATER PRESSURE BACK INTO ELECTRICITY.

A NEW RESERVOIR AT KANDERN AND A BASEL ALSTER WOULD RECOMBINE NATURE AND ENERGY!

RIEHEN

SANK

THE HORNBERG RESERVOIR IN THE BLACK FOREST WITH ITS WEHR RESERVOIR GENERATES 990MW OF ENERGY!

A RETENTION BASIN AS A NEW BASEL ALSTER (SEE PAGE 223)

HORNBERG RESERVOIR

221

AN 'ALSTER' IN BASEL

RESERVOIRS REQUIRE A LOWER RETENTION BASIN FOR ADJUSTING THE WATER LEVELS. THIS COULD BE USED FOR URBAN DEVELOPMENT BY CREATING A LAKE IN THE CITY CENTER, LIKE THE ALSTER IN HAMBURG

NEW ALSTER FOR BASEL

A LAKE IS A SOURCE OF UNIQUE QUALITY IN AN URBAN CONTEXT. ESPECIALLY WHEN IT IS COMBINED WITH MOUNTAIN SCENERY, IT CREATES A DISTINCTIVE URBAN SPACE.

BINNENALSTER AND AUSSENALSTER, HAMBURG

WOULDN'T IT BE GREAT IF WE COULD CREATE A LAKE IN THE CITY CENTER? THAT IS A LONGSTANDING PRACTICE IN URBAN DESIGN – THE ALSTER IN HAMBURG IS ALSO AN ARTIFICIAL LAKE.

BASLER-ALSTER WITH RESIDENTIAL BUILDINGS

WE COULD ENCLOSE SUCH A LAKE WITH RESIDENTIAL CONSTRUCTION.

...CYCLE AROUND THE LAKE FIVE TIMES A DAY...

223

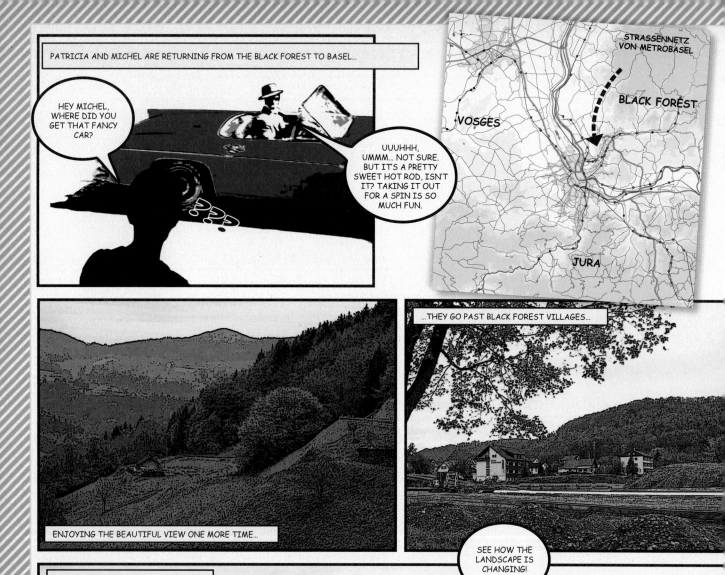

PATRICIA AND MICHEL ARE RETURNING FROM THE BLACK FOREST TO BASEL...

HEY MICHEL, WHERE DID YOU GET THAT FANCY CAR?

UUUHHH, UMMM... NOT SURE. BUT IT'S A PRETTY SWEET HOT ROD, ISN'T IT? TAKING IT OUT FOR A SPIN IS SO MUCH FUN.

STRASSENNETZ VON METROBASEL

VOSGES

BLACK FOREST

JURA

ENJOYING THE BEAUTIFUL VIEW ONE MORE TIME...

...THEY GO PAST BLACK FOREST VILLAGES...

SEE HOW THE LANDSCAPE IS CHANGING!

THE BEAUTIFUL LANDSCAPE TRIGGERS ROMANTIC FEELINGS IN PATRICIA...

WHAT A GORGEOUS DAY. MAYBE MICHEL FEELS SIMILAR AND WILL PUT HIS ARM AROUND ME?

...THROUGH HILLS AND VALLEYS...

...SOON THEY ARRIVE AT THE BORDER AND RETURN TO THE CITY CENTER...

...AND DOWN THE ROLLING HILLS...

BACK IN THE CITY, PATRICIA HAS AN IDEA:

OH YES, IF THE WEATHER IS GOOD, WE COULD GO SWIMMING IN THE RHINE LATER ON...

COME ON, LET'S GO FOR A WALK ALONG THE RIVERS OF METROBASEL.

CANAL DE HUNINGUE

IT'S A VERY POPULAR PLACE FOR WATER SPORTS AND IS DIRECTLY NORTH OF BASEL IN HUNINGUE, FRANCE..

PATRICIA AND MICHEL START IN THE NORTH OF THE CITY CENTER BY AN ARTIFICIAL RIVER: THE CANAL DE HUNINGUE IS A CHANNEL THAT FLOWS OUT OF THE RHINE, SUPPLYING WATER TO THE RHINE-RHONE CANAL.

THE BIRSIG

WE SEE HOW RIVERS LINK THE CITY AND THE SURROUNDING LANDSCAPES. ALTHOUGH, TRUTH BE TOLD, IT'S EASY TO OVERLOOK!

THE SOURCE OF THE BIRSIG IS IN THE SUNDGAU REGION OF FRANCE. IT IS THE SMALLEST OF BASEL'S RIVERS.

IN THE CITY CENTER, THE BIRSIG HAS LONG BEEN CANALIZED FOR REASONS OF HYGIENE.

THE RIVERS OF METROBASEL

THE WIESE

THE WIESE COMES DOWN TO BASEL FROM THE HILLS OF THE BLACK FOREST. IN SOME SECTIONS - SUCH AS HERE - IT FLOWS ALONGSIDE THE SWISS-GERMAN BORDER.

IT IS THE HEART OF A NEARBY RECREATION AREA. THIS IS WHERE WE FOR HIKES, BARBECUES, OR CYCLING TOURS.

THE SOURCE OF THE WIESE IS ON THE FELDBERG AT 1200M ALTITUDE. THE RIVER FLOWS SOUTH THROUGH THE WIESENTAL VALLEY UNTIL IT FEEDS INTO THE RHINE AT BASEL AFTER ABOUT 55KM AND AT 244M ALTITUDE.

MAP OF THE MAIN RIVERS OF METROBASEL

RHINE

CANAL DE HUNINGUE

WIESE

BIRSIG

ERGOLZ

BIRS

THE RIVERS OF METROBASEL ARE ASSOCIATED WITH THE THREE LANDSCAPE REGIONS: THE WIESE FROM THE BLACK FOREST, THE BIRS AND ERGOLZ FROM THE JURA, AND THE BIRSIG FROM THE SUNDGAU.

THE BIRS

OH, IT'S WONDERFUL! SO WILD AND YET AT THE SAME TIME SO CLOSE TO THE CITY CENTER

THE SOURCE OF THE BIRS IS IN THE JURA. THE RIVER MARKS THE BORDER BETWEEN BASEL-CITY AND BASEL-COUNTRY.

AT BIRSFELDEN, THE BIRS FLOWS INTO THE RHINE. THIS IS A POPULAR PLACE FOR BATHING IN THE SUMMER.

BUT THE LANDSCAPES ARE NOT LINKED TO THE CITY CENTER. THERE IS NOTHING TO INDICATE THAT BASEL IS REALLY THE GATEWAY TO THE BLACK FOREST, THE VOSGES, AND THE JURA.IST.

227

4 NEW URBAN PARKS

WE WANT TO BRING THE FOUR LAND-SCAPES INTO THE CITY!

ALSACE

BLACK FOREST

IN LANGE ERLEN, WE COULD PLANT YELLOW ANEMONES AND LUNGWORT, WHICH BLOOM IN SPRING, REPRESENTING THE BLACK FOREST IN THE CITY.

1 SPRING

1 LANGEN ERLEN

2 SUMMER

2 PARC VIGNETTE

4 HARDWALD

RHINE

POPPY PLANTS ARE TYPICAL FOR THE SUNDGAU. THEY BLOOM IN MAI AND JUNE, HERALDING SUMMER!

3 AUTUMN

...AND IN THE BRUDERHOLZ, APPLE TREES, WHICH ARE FOUND IN THE JURA.

3 BRUDERHOLZ

JURA

THE PARC VIGNETTE COULD BE PLANTED WITH TYPICAL SUNDGAU FLORA. THAT WOULD HELP BRING THIS REGION, WHICH IS SO IMPORTANT FOR BASEL, INTO THE CITY ITSELF.

SEE ALSO BASEL'S ALLOTMENT GARDENS - PAGE 61.

ALLOTMENT GARDENS AS CONNECTIONS RATHER THAN OBSTACLES

WE COULD USE THE ALLOTMENT GARDENS WITHIN THE CITY AS A CONNECTING ELEMENT BETWEEN GREEN AREAS!

GARDENS AS CONNECTIONS

THE GARDENS WIND THEIR WAY THROUGH THE CITY - NOT AS EXTENSIVE AND OB-STRUCTIVE EXPANSES, BUT RATHER LIKE BANDS. THEIR CHARACTER COULD BE MUCH MORE PUBLIC.

LANGE ERLEN REPRESENTS THE BLACK FOREST IN THE CITY

YELLOW ANEM-ONES AND LUNGWORT INDICATE THE BEGIN-NING OF SPRING. DON'T YOU GET BUTTERFLIES IN YOUR STOMACH TOO?

SPRING 1

LANGE ERLEN PARK IN SPRING

2 SUMMER

Papaver rhoeas L.

THE PARC VIGNETT REPRESENTS THE SUNDGAU IN THE CITY

SUNDGAU

PARC VIGNETTE

NOW I CAN APPRECIATE THE SUNDGAU AND THE VOSGES IN THE CITY CENTER TOO.

BRUDERHOLZ IN AUTUMN

AND IN AUTUMN, THE APPLES GROW RIPE ON THE APPLE TREES. THEY TOO MARK THE PASSING OF A SEASON. SUCH PERIODS OF MATURITY ARE OFTEN LINKED TO RITUAL EVENTS IN SOCIETY, SUCH AS THE BLOOMING OF THE CHERRY BLOSSOMS IN JAPAN.

I IMAGINE THAT THE APPLE HARVEST COULD ALSO BECOME A RECURRING EVENT IN METROBASEL. THAT WOULD ALSO ENSURE THAT THE JURA WOULD BE MORE FIRMLY ESTABLISHED IN THE PUBLIC CONSCIOUSNESS.

BRUDERHOLZ REPRESENTS JURA IN THE CITY

3 AUTUMN

Malus domestica Borkh.

JURA

FROM THE JURA!

THIS AREA, WHICH IS CURRENTLY PARTIALLY USED FOR AGRICULTURE, BUT ALSO LYING FALLOW, COULD BECOME A LARGE CITY PARK WHERE THE FLOWERS AND PLANTS OF THE JURA BRING THAT REGION INTO IMMEDIATE CONTACT WITH THE CITY.

THE HARD-WALD REPRESENTS THE RHINE IN THE CITY*

LIKE CONFETTI (RÄPPLI IN DIALECT) AT THE CARNIVAL!!!

THE SOIL OF THE HARDWALD CONSISTS MAINLY OF LIMESTONE AND SEDIMENTARY ROCKS, AND IS THUS EMBLEMATIC OF THE LANDSCAPES SHAPED BY THE RHINE.

234

RECREATION IN THE CITY CENTER

MANY PEOPLE GO TO THE KANNENFELD PARK TO RELAX

THE SCHÜTZENMATT PARK USED TO BE AN OPEN MEADOW FOR SHOOTING PRACTICE. TODAY IT IS A PARK WITH A LARGE PLAYING FIELD.

OH, THE BÄUMLIHOF AREA IS ALSO SO BEAUTIFUL. YOU HARDLY NOTICE THE CITY.

IN THE CITY CENTER, YOU CAN ALSO GO TO THE RHINE FOR RECREATION.

HEY KID! OUT OF THE WAY!

RHINE SWIM IN AUGUST

VOGEL GRYFF IN FEBRUARY

THE RHINE IS THE LOCATION OF MANY FEASTS AND TRADITIONAL RITUALS: RHINE SWIM, FESTIVA LIKE THE VOGEL GRYFF THE FIREWORKS ON T SWISS NATIONAL HOLIDAY.

RECREATION ALONG THE RHINE

BARGES ARE UNPOWERED FLOATING CONTAINERS THAT ARE OFTEN COMBINED FOR TRANSPORTING GOODS. .

SUCH COMBINATIONS OF BARGES CAN OFTEN BE SEEN HERE IN BASEL. COULDN'T WE USE THESE BARGES FOR OTHER PURPOSES AS WELL?

PUSH TOW WITH THREE PUSHED BARGES

...WOULDN'T THIS BE A GREAT WAY TO REVIVE PLACES THAT ARE NOT ACESSIBLE AT THE MOMENT - FOR EXAMPLE, NEAR BIRSFELDEN PORT OR AT AUHAFEN?

Park

SCHUBLEICHTER ALS PARK

FUMIKO, AN EXPERT ON RECREATION AT ETH STUDIO BASEL, HAS A CLEVER IDEA...

TEMPORARY BARGES AS URBAN 'PIONEERS' THAT SERVE TO ACTIVATE CERTAIN AREAS OF THE CITY.

GENEVA HAS THE BAINS DES PAQUIS. IN BASEL, WE HAVE THE BEACH BARGES!

IN PARTICULAR, BASEL'S INDUSTRIAL ZONES, WHICH ARE OFTEN LOCATED ON THE RHINE, COULD BE REMODELED THIS WAY, SUCH AS HERE AT THE AUHAFEN WITH AN ISLAND FEATURING PALM TREES AND AN ARTIFICIAL BEACH. THESE TEMPORARY INSTALLATIONS CAN ACTIVATE PLACES IN THE REGION.

MORE PUBLIC SPACES ALONG THE RHINE

NOVARTIS CAMPUS

IT WOULD BE THE FIRST STEP TOWARDS CONVERSION FROM INDUSTRIAL USE TOWARDS USAGE BY THE GENERAL POPULATION WITH RESIDENTIAL AND LEISURE AREAS.

ROSENBRÜCKE

COOL! BARGES AS A PROMENADE!

BARGES AS RHINE PROMENADES

FLOATING MARKET ON BARGES

MODEL CONCEPT

BARGE COMBINATIONS

Schwimmender Markt
Thailand

Sportbad

BARGES AS A FLOATING SWIMMING POOL

FLOATING SWIMMING POOL ON THE SPREE, BERLIN

FLOATING MARKET, THAILAND

WE COULD EASILY REUSE THE BARGES FOR OTHER PURPOSES AND MOOR THEM ALONG THE RHINE, THUS CREATING NEW PUBLIC SPACES

THAT LOOKS VERY CONVINCING. IN THIS WAY, WE WOULD ENLIVEN THE RHINE IN MANY PLACES AND MAKE IT ACCESSIBLE!!

FOR EXAMPLE, A FLOATING POOL, A HALF-PIPE FOR SKATEBOARDERS, OR A FLOATING MARKET, OR A CINEMA ON THE RIVER, OR...

THERE COULD BE LOTS OF NEW ACTIVITIES ALONG THE RHINE.

Schubleichter
Ausbauvarianten

ERIK, THE EXPERT FOR MOBILITY, CONFIRMS THE POTENTIALS

ICE SKATING ON THE RHINE

DECEMBER
10
WINTER

245

THE DEVELOPMENT OF METRO BASEL

IT'S IMPORTANT TO POINT OUT THAT WHAT MATTERS IS NOT JUST EXCELLENT ARCHITECTURE, BUT AN OPEN MIND AND THE WILLINGNESS TO KEEP TRYING OUT NEW IDEAS.

FRANCIS IS A FORMER STUDENT OF ETH STUDIO BASEL.

URSULA KOCH, THE FORMER DIRECTOR OF THE CITY OF ZURICH'S DEPARTMENT OF PUBLIC WORKS, SAID IN 1986:

NO!!! THAT'S WRONG!

"...THE CITY IS BUILT...!"*

A CITY IS NEVER COMPLETELY BUILT. IT IS ALWAYS UNDERGOING CHANGE, AND THAT IS HOW IT SHOULD BE! WE'VE SEEN THAT MUCH OF WHAT WE TODAY REGARD AS NORMAL, HISTORIC, AND ESTABLISHED WAS REALLY A RADICAL INTERVENTION AT THE TIME, AND REPLACED OLDER STRUCTURES. WE'VE ALSO SEEN THAT THERE IS A HUGE POTENTIAL FOR CHANGING THE REGION AND INTRODUCING NEW QUALITIES; POSSIBILITIES THAT HAVE NEVER BEEN CONSIDERED BEFORE. WE SHOULD REGARD THESE CHANGES AS A POSITIVE THING AND AS AN OPPORTUNTIY TO DO GREAT NEW THINGS IN THE REGION. THE CITY IS NEVER COMPLETELY BUILT!

*SHE MEANT TO SAY THAT A CITY SUCH AS ZURICH IS 'COMPLETE' AND NEED NOT UNDERGO ANY MORE MAJOR CHANGES.

A MINDSET THAT IS OPEN TO CHANGE AND REGARDS ARCHITECTURE AND URBANISM...

...AS A POTENTIAL FOR TRANSFORMATION...

...IS VERY IMPORTANT TO US!

GOETHEANUM

RONCHAMP BY LE CORBUSIER

SECONDARY SCHOOL BY WALTER FÖRDERER

BIRSFELDEN POWER PLANT BY HANS HOFMANN

VITRA FIRESTATION BY ZAHA HADID

IBA Basel 2020
Trinationale Stadtregion entdecken
Memorandumsentwurf

HERE WE SEE A SELECTION OF VISIONARY AND UNUSUAL ARCHITECTURE IN METROBASEL. THIS SHOWS HOW IMPORTANT IT IS TO ADMIT CHANGE AND USE THE POTENTIAL THAT A REGION HAS TO OFFER. ANOTHER GOOD EXAMPLE IS THE INTERNATIONAL BUILDING EXHIBITION IN BASEL, PLANNED FOR 2020!

BRIDGE WITH PEOPLE'S HALL (SEE PAGE 237)

THE TRINATIONAL REGION OF BASEL AIMS TO USE THE FORMAT OF AN INTERNATIONAL BUILDING EXHIBITION TO REALIZE HIGH-QUALITY PROJECTS WITH THE AIM OF GIVING SUSTAINABLE GUIDANCE TO THE GROWTH OF THE REGION, TO AFFIRM TRANS-BOUNDARY ENGAGEMENT, AND TO ENHANCE THE VISIBILITY OF THE REGION BOTH DOMESTICALLY AND ABROAD.

FRANCESCA FERGUSON IS THE DIRECTOR OF THE SWISS ARCHITECTURE MUSEUM, WHICH IS LOCATED IN BASEL

249

ARCHITECTURE IN METROBASEL

79

78

77

76

75

BURGHOF THEATER, LÖRRACH (D), W. & K. STEIB, 1998

73

72

71

WITH A VIEW, RHINE PORT (CH), BERNOULLI, 1923

37

VITRA PRODUKTION WEIL AM RHEIN, D SANAA, 2009

VITRA FIRE STATION, WEIL AM RHEIN (D), ZAHA HADID, 1992

THOMI & FRANCK BASEL, CH, 1967 BURCKHARDT & PARTNER

RESIDENTIAL ESTATE SCHORENMATTEN, BASEL (CH), HANS SCHMIDT, 1929

VITRA DESIGN MUSEUM WEIL AM RHEIN (D) FRANK GEHRY, 1989

FONDATION BEYELER, RIEHEN (CH), RENZO PIANO, 1998

33

EXHIBITION TOWER, BASEL (CH), MORGER & DEGELO

BRÜCKE, 1903

32

69

31

POWER PLANT BIRSFELDEN (CH), H. HOFMANN, 1954

YOU JUMP IN THE RHINE AND DRIFT DOWNSTREAM...

SEL CITY HALL OM 1503 ON

LONZA HOUSE, BASEL (CH), SUTER+SUTER, 1962

"TART"

GELLERTKIRCHE, BASEL (CH), C.P. BLUMER, 1964

29

TINGUELY MUSEUM, BASEL (CH), MARIO BOTTA, 1996

67

66

OUSE,

SIGNAL BOX, BASEL (CH) 1990, HERZOG & DE MEURON

65

WOW, THAT'S A LOT OF EXCITING, EXPERI-MENTAL, AND VISIONARY ARCHITECTURE. METROBASEL SEEMS PRETTY UNIQUE IN THIS RESPECT. WE CER-TAINLY HAVE TO SEE IT ALL.

FREIDORF ESTATE, MUTTENZ (CH), H. MEYER, 1919

27

SCHAULAGER, 2003 MÜNCHENSTEIN (CH) HERZOG & DE MEURON

64

63

GOETHEANUM DORNACH (CH) R. STEINER, 1925

RESIDENTIAL BUILD-ING, 2004, AESCH (CH), BUCHNER BRÜNDLER

SECONDARY SCHOOL, AESCH (CH), W. FÖRDERER, 1960

ARLESHEIM CATHE-DRAL, ARLESHEIM (CH), JAKOB ENGEL, 1681

251

WE'VE TRAVELLED AROUND THE CITY AND ITS ENVIRONS FOR A WEEK, AND SEEN AND LEARNED AN INCREDIBLE LOT OF THINGS.

NOW WE SHOULD SUMMARIZE OUR IDEAS FOR METROBASEL: HOW IT MIGHT DEVELOP IN THE FUTURE AND WHICH STEPS WE THINK ARE NECESSARY:

THAT'S A GOOD IDEA. IT'S PROBABLY BEST TO DO SO IN THE SEQUENCE OF HOW WE EXPLORED THE CITY, AND TO TAKE SOME NOTES ALONG THE WAY.

THE CORE CITY AND ITS REGIONS

WE NOTICED QUICKLY THAT THE RHINE SHOULD BE INTEGRATED MUCH MORE CLOSELY WITH THE LIVES AND ACTIVITIES OF THE RESIDENTS. THE RIVER SHOULD BE ACCESSIBLE EVERYWHERE AND BECOME THE TRUE CENTER OF METROBASEL.

WE ALSO HAVE TO WORK TO ENSURE THAT THE REGION IS BETTER INTERCONNECTED AT ALL LEVELS, SO THAT BORDERS DON'T FORM OBSTACLES, BUT BECOME AN ASSET!

ACROSS THE ENTIRE REGION, THERE IS A LOT OF MEDIOCRITY; WHAT WE SHOULD DO IS AIM FOR MORE HIGH-END AS WELL AS MORE LOW-END QUALITY IN ALL AREAS. THAT WOULD INCREASE THE RANGE OF OPTIONS IN THE REGION!

THE ISSUE OF LIVING SPACE IS VERY IMPORTANT. BASEL NEEDS MORE ATTRACTIVE RESIDENTIAL AREAS – FOR EXAMPLE, ALONG THE RHINE.

THE MOST BEAUTIFUL SPACES, WHICH ARE CURRENTLY STILL OCCUPIED BY INDUSTRY AND ALLOTMENT PLOTS, SHOULD BE TURNED INTO RESIDENTIAL ZONES.

IN THE CITY CENTER, WE CAN DENSIFY THE RESIDENTIAL AREAS. IN A CITY LIKE BASEL, HIGHER BUILDINGS AND MORE AMALGAMATION WOULD BE FITTING. MANY CITIES DEMONSTRATE HOW HIGHER DENSITY COINCIDES WITH QUALITY OF LIFE!

LIVING

METROBASEL ALSO NEEDS A BROADER RANGE OF OPTIONS FOR LIVING SPACE. CURRENTLY, THERE IS A LOT OF MEDIOCRITY IN THIS AREA. WHAT IS NEEDED IS CHEAPER LIVING SPACE...

...APARTMENTS THAT ARE LESS CONVENTIONALLY DESIGNED SUCH AS LOFTS, AND WE NEED MORE LUXURY APARTMENTS, VILLAS, AND COUNTRY HOUSES, WHICH ARE CURRENTLY ALMOST COMPLETELY ABSENT IN THE REGION.

WORKING

HOW UNFORTU- NATE THAT MANY INDUS- TRIAL AREAS AND WORK PLACES ARE SITUATED AT BASEL'S MOST ATTARCTIVE LOCATIONS. THEY SHOULD BE RELOCATED SO THAT THE SITES CAN BE CONVERTED, SUCH AS THE RHINE PORTS, OR THE RAILWAY'S LOGISTICS AREAS AND THE DREISPITZ ESTATE.

THE CLUSTERING OF ECONOMIC SECTORS IS IMPORTANT FOR THE REGION AND FOR THE COMPANIES THEM- SELVES. THIS IS SOMETHING WE SHOULD STEER AND FOSTER, USING COMPANIES AS URBANISTIC ACTORS.

MOVING

FIRST OF ALL, THE S-BAHN NEEDS TO BE EX- TENDED TO THE CITY CENTER AS SOON AS POSSIBLE. WE CALL THIS PROJECT THE 'HERZSTÜCK URBAN RAILWAY'. IT IS CRUCIAL FOR TRI- NATIONAL DEVELOPMENT AND THE REGION'S INTEGRATION WITH THE NUCLEATED CITY!

NEXT, WE NOTICED THE DIVISIVE EFFECTS OF INFRA- STRUCTURE LINES. WE SHOULD COME UP WITH NEW BUILDING TYPES FOR BUILDING OVER THESE TRAFFIC SPACES AND RECON- NECTING THE CITY MORE CLOSELY.

THESE COULD BE PARKS BUILT ACROSS THE HIGHWAYS AND RAIL TRACKS, OR BUILDINGS CONVERTING A TRAFFIC INTERSECTION INTO A THREE-DIMENSIONAL, DENSE, LIVELY CITYSCAPE.

AND FINALLY WE NEED TO BUILD MORE BRIDGES ACROSS THE RHINE TO CONNECT THE CITY QUAR- TERS AND THE THREE COUNTRIES MORE CLOSELY. THE THREE-COUN- TRY BRIDGE CONNECTING WEIL AND HUNINGUE IS A GOOD EXAMPLE.

WE ALSO RE- ALLY LIKE THE IDEA OF BROADENING MITTLERE BRÜCKE INTO A PUBLIC SQUARE IN THE MIDDLE OF THE RHINE. IT WOULD BE HARD TO IMAGINE A MORE BEAUTIFUL PLACE IN BASEL!

SHOPPING

I NOTICED WHILE SHOPPING THAT THE TOP AND BOTTOM MARKET SEGMENTS ARE NOT WELL REPRE- SENTED. THERE OUGHT TO BE MORE HIGH-END SHOPS WITH EXCLUSIVE GOODS AND MORE INTERESTING AND INNOVATIVE AFFORDABLE SHOPS. AT THE MOMENT, THERE IS TOO MUCH MEDIOCRITY.

THERE ALSO OUGHT TO BE A BETTER MARKET FOR FRESH GOODS IN BASEL. THERE ARE MANY EXAMPLES IN OTHER CIT- IES OF HOW THIS COULD BE DONE QUITE ATTARC- TIVELY. THE EXISITING MARKET IS PRETTY MODEST.

253

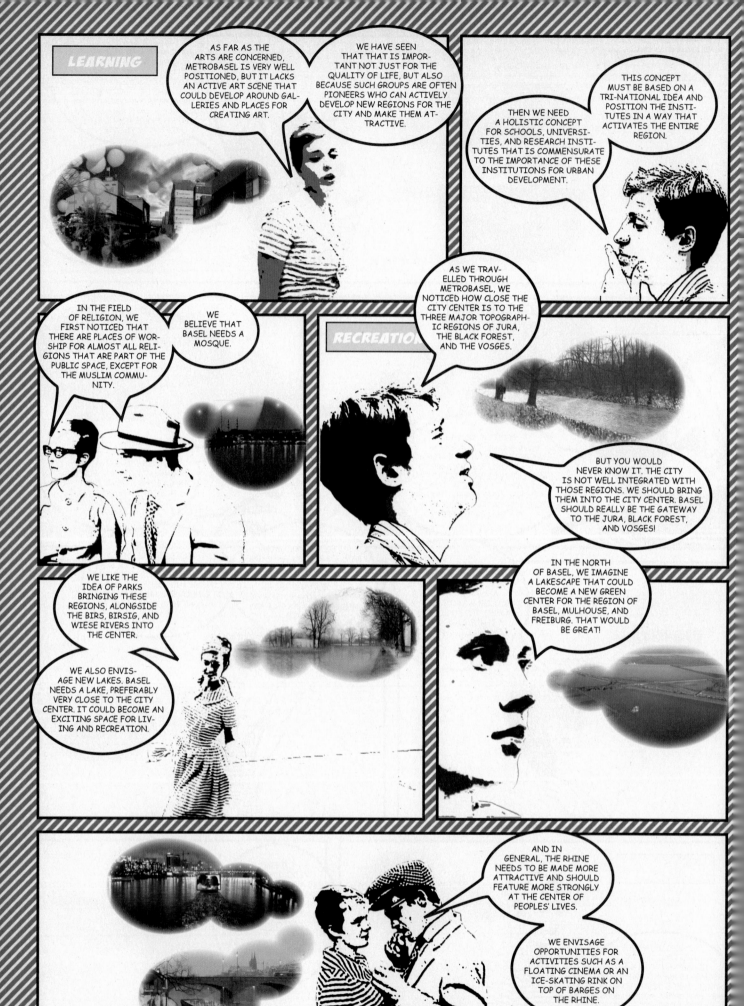

AIMS

WE ARE HOPING FOR A REGION WHERE ITS TRI-NATIONAL QUALITY IS NOT A HINDRANCE, BUT AN ACTIVE POTENTIAL. WE BELIEVE THAT NATURE IS PART OF THE CITY, BUT THAT IT CAN ALSO BE CHANGED TO FEATURE NEW RIVERS, LAKES, HILLS, AND PARKS.

IT IS A REGION THAT CAN CHANGE. HERE EVEN VISIONARY AND EXPERIMENTAL PROPOSALS IN ARCHITECTURE AND URBANISM CAN BE REALIZED!

...SO LET'S SEE WHAT WE ARE TRYING TO ACHIEVE FOR BASEL AND THE TRI-NATIONAL REGION:

AIMS FOR METROBASEL:

LIVING:
- 15,000 ADDITIONAL APARTMENTS IN BASEL-STADT!
- LIVING HAS TO TAKE PLACE ALONG THE RHINE! INDUSTRY AND ALOTMENT GARDENS SHOULD BE RELOCATED.
- MORE AFFORDABLE APARTMENTS AND MORE EXCLUSIVE RESIDENTIAL SPACES. WE HAVE TOO MUCH MEDIOCRITY!

WORKING:
- ALL HARBORS SHOULD RELOCATE TO THE NORTH OF BASEL.
- TRANSFORM INDUSTRIAL ZONES INTO MIXED URBAN AREAS. THESE AREAS CAN HAVE A HIGH DENSITY OF DIVERSE URBAN PROGRAMS.

MOVING:
- COVERING INFRASTRUCTURE WITH NEW PARKS OR WITH MIXED USE AREAS IN ORDER TO TIE THE CITY CLOSER TOGETHER.
- THE S-BAHN 'HERZSTÜCK' WITH THE NORTHERN LINK HAS TO BE BUILT!
- WE WANT A TRI-NATIONAL LOCAL TRANSPORT SYSTEM WITH TRAMS.

SHOPPING:
- INNERCITY SHOPPING HAS TO BE CURATED. METROBASEL NEEDS THE BEST SHOPS AS WELL AS AFFORDABLE AND INNOVATIVE STORES!
- WE WANT A GREAT FOOD COURT AND BETTER URBAN MARKETS.

LEARNING:
- BASEL NEEDS A YOUNG ART SCENE. SPACES FOR ART PRODUCTION AND ART GALLERIES WHICH CAN ACT AS URBAN PIONEERS.
- BASEL UNIVERSITY SHOULD OPERATE TRI-NATIONALLY AND BE EMBEDDED IN A CONTEXT OF SWISS, FRENCH AND GERMAN HIGH-END RESEARCH CENTERS.
- BASEL NEEDS AN OPERA!
- BASEL NEEDS A MOSQUE!

RECREATION:
- BASEL NEEDS A LAKE IN THE CITY CENTER!
- WE WANT A 'CENTRAL PARK' WITH A DENSE SURROUNDING CITY FABRIC
- THE CORE CITY SHOULD BE UNDERSTOOD AS THE GATE TO THE NEARBY LANDSCAPE REGIONS OF JURA, BLACK FOREST AND THE VOSGES!

THE CORE CITY AND THE TRI-NATIONAL REGION:
- WE HAVE TO PLAN AND DESIGN TRI-NATIONALLY!
- A CLOSELY LINKED TRI-NATIONAL REGION WHICH UNDERSTANDS THE CORE CITY AND ITS SURROUNDINGS AS A UNIT, BRINGING TOGETHER THE INDIVIDUAL PARTS.
- NATURE IS PART OF OUR SHAPED AND CULTIVATED ENVIRONMENT. WE WANT TO SHAPE THIS NATURE, ESPECIALLY REGARDING THE FUTURE, WITH ITS CHANCES, PROBLEMS AND CHALLENGES!

BASEL NORTH

LIVING ON THE RHINE

LIVING ON THE RHINE

CENTRAL PARK

TRI-NATIONAL PORT

PARK-COVERED

INFRASTRUCTURE

ART CENTER

ST. LOUIS

DREISPITZ QUARTER

GREEN PATHS TO

THE RHINE

WELLNESS IN THE CITY

CENTRE

SHOPPING IN THE CITY

CENTRE

MARKET AS A

SHOPPING EXPERIENCE

FLOATING

CINEMA

ICE SKATING ON THE BARGE

MITTLERE BRÜCKE...

..AS A PLAZA

ON THE RHINE

HILL OF BASEL

HARDWALD

LANGE ERLEN

BASEL ALSTER

LAKESCAPE

BLACK FOREST

RESERVOIRS

WE ARE THANKFUL FOR THE IDEAS, THE INPUT AND FOR THE ORGANIZATIONAL SUPPORT

BY THE DEPARTMENT OF PRESIDENTIAL AFFAIRS BASEL-STADT WITH GUY MORIN, MARKUS RITTER, THOMAS KESSLER, AND ANDREAS PECNIK; KANTONSBAUMEISTER BASEL-STADT, FRITZ SCHUMACHER; THE METROBASEL ASSOCIATION WITH CHRISTOPH KOELLREUTER; THE TRINATIONAL EURODISTRICT BASEL TEB WITH FRÉDÉRIC DUVINAGE; THE ADMINISTRATIONS OF DISTRICT LÖRRACH, CANTON HUNINGUE AND CANTON BASEL-LAND; THE DEPARTMENT OF EDUCATION BASEL-STADT WITH HANS GEORG SIGNER; THE FORMER CANTONAL ARCHEOLOGIST ROLF D'AUJOURD'HUI AND HIS COLLEAGUE CHRISTINE HATZ; THE STATISTICAL DEPARTMENT OF CANTON BASEL-STADT WITH ULRICH GRÄF AND NATHALIE GRILLON; THE UNIVERSITY OF BASEL WITH BEAT MÜNCH AND RAOUL FURLANO; THE HISTORICAL MUSEUM OF BASEL WITH FRANZ EGGER AND ANDREAS FISCHER; THE DIRECTOR OF THE SWISS ARCHITECTURE MUSEUM FRANCESCA FERGUSON; CAY-SOPHIE RABINOWITZ FOR HER IDEAS IN THE FIELD OF ART, AND DAVINDER LAMBA WHOSE COMIC WAS VERY INSPIRATIONAL FOR US.

WE ARE ALSO THANKFUL TO SHADI RAHBARAN, LIGIA NOBRE, ANN-SOFI RÖNNSKOG, MILICA TOPALOVIC, ROGER DIENER, MARCEL MEILI, CHRISTIAN SCHMID, EMANUEL CHRIST, SIMON HARTMANN, JOHN PALMESINO, MARTIN JOSEPHY AND THE WHOLE TEAM OF ETH STUDIO BASEL

FUMIKO TAKAHAMA IS RESPONSIBLE FOR THE BEAUTIFULLY PAINTED DRAWINGS. ISABELLE ABELE, HILLA RUDANKO AND JERONIMO MEJIA HAVE SUPPORTED US ADMINISTRATIVELY. LITTLE FLORINA HAS POSED AS MODEL.

WE ARE VERY HAPPY ABOUT THE COLLABORATION WITH HARVARD - GRADUATE SCHOOL OF DESIGN, WITH TOSHIKO MORI WHO ORGANIZED THE BASEL-PROJECT, AND THE GENEROUS SUPPORT BY ELISE JAFFE UND JEFFREY BROWN.

WE ARE THANKFUL FOR ALL WHO HAVE CONTRIBUTED WITH THEIR IDEAS, INFORMATION, CRITIQUE AND SUGGESTIONS IN DISCUSSIONS, JURIES AND REVIEWS. WE ESPECIALLY WANT TO THANK ALL STUDENTS:

DAN BACIU, MICHAEL BUSCHOR, DAIANA CAMASTRA, FRANCIS FAWCETT, RETO GSELL, KATHRIN HASLER, THOMAS HUBER, DONG GYU KIM, EVERT KLINKENBERT, CLAUDIA MÜHLEBACH, SEBASTIAN PATER, FILIP PAVEL, NATALIE POMER, FLORIAN POPPELE, ANJA STÜRCHLER, MULAN SUN, SOLEY SUTER, ANGELA WAIBEL, CLAUDIO WASER, ANDRI WERLEN, THOMAS WÖLFEL, LORENZO GIACOMO ZANCHETTA, LIBEI ZHAO, ROMAN ZIEGLER, NICOLAI RÜNZI, LEOPOLD WEINBERG, MAI KOMURO, CHARLOTTE VON MOOS, CHRISTIAN MUELLER INDERBITZEN, KONRAD GRASER, LUKAS KUENG, RAMIAS STEINEMANN, ISABELLE BENTZ, MARIN LEISI, PHILIPPE VOLP, ANDREAS FLUCK, RAPHAEL KRÄUTLER, CHARLES WÜLSER, LEA GNOEPFF, RETO KELLER MIGUEL MEIRINHOS, MAIKO HANN, MATTHIAS BAUMGÄRTNER, JOHANES GELD, JONAS WUEST, GEORG SCHMID, FLORIAN GRAF, SOOHYUN CHANG, OLIVER COOKE, GUY NAHUM, ERIK TIETZ, GEE GHID TSE.

LAST BUT NOT LEAST, WE OBVIOUSLY WANT TO THANK JEAN SEBERG AND JEAN-PAUL BELMONDO, AS WELL AS JEAN-LUC GODARD.

JACQUES HERZOG, PIERRE DE MEURON, MANUEL HERZ UND YING ZHOU